DIARY OF A DISCIPLE:

LUKE'S STORY

Gemma Willis

Illustrated by Emma Randall

Copyright © Scripture Union 2016
First published 2016, reprinted 2016

ISBN 978 1 78506 470 8

The right of Gemma Willis to be identified as author of this work has been asserted by her in accordance with the Copyright, Designs and Patents Act 1988.

Emma Randall has asserted her right under the Copyright, Designs and Patents Act 1988, to be identified as illustrator of this work.

British Library Cataloguing-in-Publication Data. A catalogue record of this book is available from the British Library.

Printed in India by Thomson Press India Ltd

Cover and internal design by Emma Randall

Scripture Union is an international Christian charity working with churches in more than 130 countries.

Thank you for purchasing this book. Any profits from this book support SU in England and Wales to bring the good news of Jesus Christ to children, young people and families and to enable them to meet God through the Bible and prayer.

Find out more about our work and how you can get involved at:
www.scriptureunion.org.uk (England and Wales)
www.suscotland.org.uk (Scotland)
www.suni.co.uk (Northern Ireland)
www.scriptureunion.org (USA)
www.su.org.au (Australia)

CHAPTER 1

FANCY A CHAT?

GOOD EVENING,

and a very warm welcome to my

MARVELLOUS STORY.

My name is Luke. **Dr Luke**, actually. And I have been carefully _investigating_ a series of mysterious events. And because I'm a bit of a **NERD**, I've decided to write all of my investigations down, just for you. **Lots** of other people have **tried** to write it all down before, but I want you to hear **my** side of the story.

SO, it all starts with a woman called _Elizabeth_.

FACT FILE

NAME: Elizabeth

FAMILY: Zechariah (husband)

Mary (cousin)

NUMBER OF CHILDREN: 0

AGE: Very old

LOCATION: Lives in a little house up a hill in Judea

FACT FILE

NAME: Zechariah

FAMILY: Elizabeth (wife)

NUMBER OF CHILDREN: 0

AGE: Very old

LOCATION: Very important Temple in Jerusalem

Elizabeth was **very old**. She was married to

Zechariah (who was also very old), who was a kind of

special religious leader **GUY** and he worked with a group

of other special vicars who took it in turns to burn

smelly stuff in the **TEMPLE**

(kind of like a Jewish church). ANYWAY it was

Zechariah's turn to do the burning (he burned incense

— that's the **smelly stuff** — as a way of helping people

to **WORSHIP** God) and while he was inside on his

own, something **ABSOLUTELY** "TERRIFYING" happened.

A large, glowing, bright man-shaped thing appeared out

of nowhere and said,

The man said, "You and your wife are going to have a

BABY called **John**." Zechariah thought this

guy was crazy, and pretty much told him so

– which was a bit of a mistake. OOPS.

Because then the man introduced himself as the

ANGEL GABRIEL

(still scary!) and told Zechariah he'd not be able to

talk until John was born.

NOTE TO SELF – <u>always</u> listen to what angels say,

AND DO AS TOLD.

As a Doctor I can tell you that I'd have thought it all

sounded a bit crazy too, I mean super Old people

don't just suddenly start having babies.

It doesn't WORK that way!

6

Poor Zechariah had to invent his OWN version of

sign language

so that he could tell everyone what had happened to him.

When he FINALLY got home to Elizabeth and

managed to wave his arms around enough so that she could

understand what had happened, she was even more

AMAZED

than he was.

6 months later

the **ANGEL GABRIEL** was out and about again, only this time he was in a (TINY) town called **N**azareth, having a chat with a woman called

MARY.

He was telling her all sorts of *lovely* things (that God had told him to say), so he couldn't understand why Mary seemed SO SCARED. I mean, what's scary about being told that God "really likes you", that he's with you and that you're going to have A BABY and God's going to be the DAD... and you have to call him JESUS? That's not scary at all... if you're the angel Gabriel. Gabriel also said, "Oh, by the way, your cousin *Elizabeth* is having a BABY too." Mary took a DEEP BREATH and calmly said, "OK. If it's what God wants, then I'LL DO IT." She must've been SUPER brave.

MARY went to see *Elizabeth* and she was definitely pregnant, either that or she'd eaten a GIANT FOOTBALL for breakfast. Elizabeth was SO EXCITED to see Mary that both she and baby John JUMPED up and down for JOY, and Mary started to dance and sing:

God is **SO GOOD**, I can hardly believe it

Why'd he choose me, I'm really not a good fit

But he has *blessed* me, because he is epic

And I will praise him, 'cos he's FANTASTIC

10

He's **SO** good, he's **SO** kind

I can't believe he had me on his mind

He's **SO AWESOME**, he's **SO STRONG**

It's amazing he's *loved* us all for so long

God is **SO GOOD**, I can hardly believe it,

He has chosen **ME**, so now I'll do my bit

He's my *helper*, he's my **LORD**

He is **GOD**, he's the Lord of all!

EVENTUALLY, Elizabeth had her baby and everyone told her she should call him **ZECHARIAH** after his dad. Elizabeth tried to tell them all she wanted to call him **John**, but they were having **NONE OF IT**. Zechariah started waving his arms about like **crazy** again and everyone stared at him. **WEIRDO**. Then he grabbed something to write on and scribbled down something that looked vaguely like

Joan, or maybe Joon or, maybe, Jobo.

But eventually someone said, "Does that say **John**?

12

PRAISE GOD!" At that moment Zechariah suddenly blurted out: "John! John! John! His name is John!" then he pulled a rather ODD face and said, "Hey! Did I just say that out loud?"

Everyone stopped and stared at old Zechariah. He hadn't said a SINGLE word for 9 whole months (not even a THANK YOU – how rude!) and then all of a SUDDEN he could speak again. Super CONFUSING eh? But the people began to wonder...

There must be something special about this John baby, maybe God might've had something to do with it...

Baby John became the subject of village gossip pretty quickly!

Zechariah was <u>SO EXCITED</u> at being able to talk again,

that words just wouldn't stop coming out of his mouth.

He was **happy**, sorry, EXCITED, exhäusted and **AMAZED** all at once.

God has done it <u>again!</u>

He's really Saving us all

Just like he said he would

He **NEVER** breaks a promise.

He's **RESCUING** us,

He's **FORGIVING** us,

He's **LOVING** us,

He's **AMAZING!**

"And John," (Zechariah "BOUNCED" him on his

knee as he said this),

you're going to be the <u>start</u>

of it ALL! You're going to tell

people what's coming, you're

going to be like a signpost.

(Very INSPIRATIONAL

comment from a father there.)

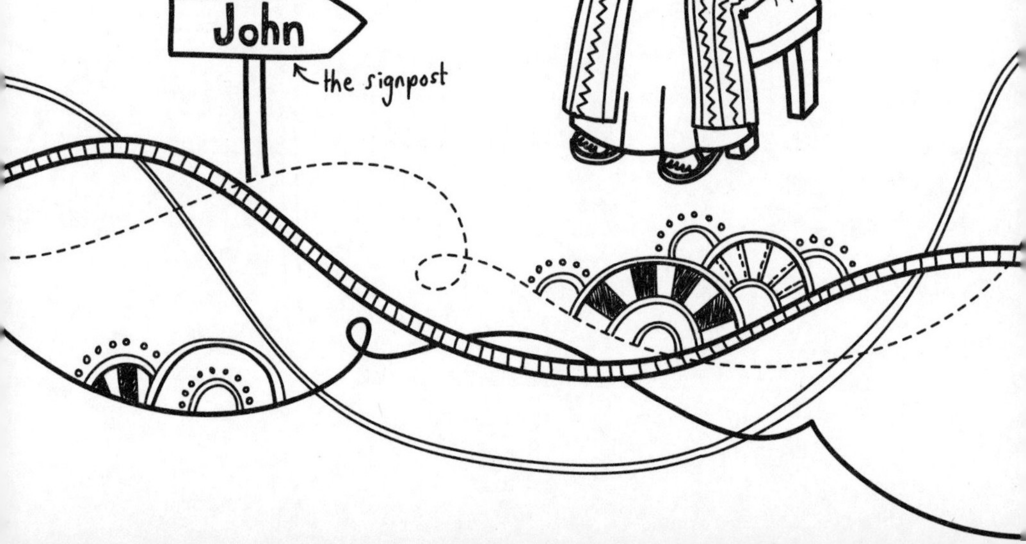

John

↖ the signpost

As John grew up, he was still a **HOT TOPIC**  in the local **gossip** charts, especially when he decided to go off and live in the desert, wear **CAMEL** hair and _eat_ only **HONEY** and insects. Tasty. How was he supposed to be a signpost in the desert? No one ever even went there!

CHAPTER 2

PIGEONS & RAISINS

So, ANYWAY, back to babies again. Some

man named AUGUSTUS

(seriously, that's a bad name... but it's got

to be better than DECEMBERUS) decided

he wanted to make an ENORMOUS

list of names, places and people.

The only way Augustus could figure out who

was who was to ask people to travel ALL

the way back to where they were born and sign

up on the list in each TOWN. Can you imagine

how long the queues were? Boring...

So, even though **MARY** was getting to be the size of a small **HOUSE**, because she was engaged to Joe (a local carpenter), they both had to get themselves off ⇨ to **B**ethlehem (that's where Joe was born).

DID YOU KNOW:

Joe's GREAT grandad (×**38** greats!) was called David.

In fact, most people knew him as **KING DAVID** (he once killed a giant called **GOLIATH** by throwing a pebble in

ⒹⓄ ouch!

his face — no seriously — he did: you can check it out in a

Bible in 1 Samuel 17) and he was born in Bethlehem, too.

How **AWESOME** is that? Coincidence?? Or all part of

the plan??

Welcome to Bethlehem!

When they FINALLY arrived, Mary was getting

pretty UNCOMFORTABLE (Ewww...) when the

baby decided to announce HE WAS ON HIS WAY.

She sent Joe off to find them somewhere to stay — it

was pretty URGENT...

owch!

Joe RUSHED back to Mary and said he'd found

✰✰✰✰✰

them a FIVE-STAR place to share with a few others

very nice

that had great en-suite facilities and free snacks.

sweet!

UNFORTUNATELY, it turned out that Joe hadn't quite

:)

understood what he'd been told. They ended up in a place

that certainly had one very bright star shining above

it, and there were DEFINITELY others that they had to share

with, except they weren't people — they were animals!

moooo *eeorr* *baaa*

The en-suite facilities were great for the cows and sheep,
but Mary and Joe didn't enjoy the **SMELL**
...Stinky! And the free snacks? Well, if you're a cow or
a sheep then hay makes a **FANTASTIC** snack,
but for Mary and Joe – a bit **chewy.**

The hay might not have been **Tasty**, but it gave Mary a
great idea. She wrapped her new baby in a
scratchy blanket and used the hay to
make him a kind of nest in the animals'
feed box. The sheep seemed pretty interested in their new
snack, but Mary made sure they didn't nibble more than
A FEW TOES... Mary named the baby **JESUS**,
just as the angel had said.

While Mary was trying to get the NEW BABY to fall asleep, some SHEPHERDS nearby were desperately trying to stay awake... yawn. Someone had to keep WATCH to make sure the sheep didn't get gobbled up by (monsters)... well, by WOLVES or something.

Just as the shepherds' eyes were beginning to close they were almost blinded by a SUPER BRIGHT LIGHT. They screwed their eyes up tightly and squinted at something BIG and WHITE and SHINY. The shiny something started to talk and the shepherds were ABSOLUTELY TERRIFIED. It said: "Don't be scared, I'm here to tell you something super awesome. Just over those hills in the town where KING DAVID was

22

born all those years ago, a new baby is lying in a nest made of hay, wrapped in a scratchy blanket and waiting to meet you! He was born for you, in fact he's going to **SAVE** you because he is the Saviour, the Messiah, the **LORD!**"

The shepherds looked at each other, then looked back at the **SHINY** thing, then looked back at each other and said, "Erm... I think that's an **ANGEL!**"

BEFORE they had time to answer loads of other shiny guys appeared and started *singing* - so **LOUD** that even when the shepherds put their fingers in their ears they could still hear EVERY WORD...

GOD is so AMAZING, he's worth more than ANYTHING EVER
He's bringing Peace to ALL on EARTH and so we sing together

GOD is so AMAZING, he's worth more than ANYTHING EVER
He's bringing Peace to ALL on EARTH and so we sing together

GOD is so AMAZING, he's worth more than ANYTHING EVER
He's bringing Peace to ALL on EARTH and so we sing together

GOD is so AMAZING, he's worth more than ANYTHING EVER
He's bringing Peace to ALL on EARTH and so we sing together

By now, the shepherds had figured out that these were **IN FACT** angels and, because they'd heard that if an angel gave you a message from **GOD**, you (should) do it, they decided that maybe they ought to go and visit this baby.

When they arrived in Bethlehem the shepherds were

AMAZED. There he was, this (TINY) little baby lying

in a nest of hay in a place that cows *(moooo)* and sheep *(baaah)* had made

smell quite... i**N**te**RES**t**i**NG *(hmmm)*... The shepherds decided

they should probably tell Mary what the ANGELS

had said about this baby being :special: being a saviour,

in fact the SAVIOUR, the MESSIAH, the LORD.

Joe was slightly confused and thought perhaps the shepherds

needed some *sleep* zzzzzzzz, but Mary listened to what

they said and she began to WONDER...

25

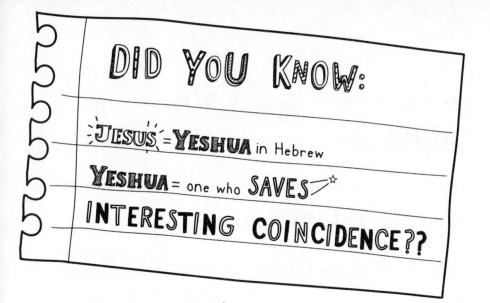

DID YOU KNOW:

JESUS = YESHUA in Hebrew

YESHUA = one who SAVES ☆

INTERESTING COINCIDENCE??

The shepherds SUDDENLY realised they'd been away from

their ⦃sheep⦄ for quite a while, and remembered they were

SUPPOSED to be protecting them from ~~monsters~~ WOLVES.

They RAN all the way back to their fields, but they were

so EXCITED by what they'd seen that they couldn't resist

jumping UP and DOWN and DANCING as they went.

Let me ASSURE you, shepherd dancing is like the WORST

kind of dancing you can imagine. Majorly embarrassing. Just NO.

But the shepherds just DIDN'T CARE, they were SOOOOO

EXCITED, and they tried to remember the song the angels

had been singing earlier.

GOD is so AMAZING, he's worth more than ANY of my SHEEP

He's bringing Peace to ALL on EARTH and soon we'll go to sleep

(Don't CHEAT and turn back the page — can you

remember what the angels sang?)

A few days later Mary and Joe took Jesus into the CITY. They had to take him to the TEMPLE and officially name him. STRANGELY, they also had to take 2 pigeons with them. We'll call them PLOPPY and Prunella.

Although (maybe) we shouldn't name them... (Want to know **WHY?** You can find out in a Bible *in* Leviticus 12:6-8)

When Mary and Joe arrived at the Temple, an OLD WRINKLY man called SIMEON was waiting for them.

Mary and Joe had **never** met Simeon before, but he said that GOD had told him to come to the Temple and wait for them to bring Jesus along. **SUDDENLY** Simeon grabbed Jesus, held him *high* up in the air and swung him round and round until he was super dizzy.

Mary and Joe were just about to POLITELY remove

Jesus from this _rather_ PECULIAR old man

when he SUDDENLY began to SING:

I'm a servant of GOD

The ONE and ONLY GOD

He's the (only) one who could

And I just KNEW he would

He's sent the world a Saviour

To LIGHT the way for all

And now I've seen him on my own

I know I'm ready to go HOME

Mary and Joe held on to Ploppy and Prunella in their pigeon box and watched the old man in ✩AMAZEMENT.✩ He sang and sang and twirled Jesus around and around for what seemed like (hours). Joe was beginning to WONDER if he'd ever stop when ✩SUDDENLY✩ he turned to Mary and said:

This child will do amazing things,

(Mary thought that sounded good),

but not everyone will like him.

(Mary and Joe wondered HOW the old man could know that and thought it was bit MEAN to say such a thing about (Jesus) while he was only a baby — I mean, he could turn out all right couldn't he ❓) Simeon carried on,

He's going to do things you'd never imagine,

(that sounded good again),

but Mary you'll **SUFFER** because of him,

you really will...

(WHAT?!?)

Simeon handed Jesus back to Mary and **wandered** off.

Joe was just about to suggest that they went **HOME**

before Simeon came back when a (TINY) *Old* lady walked

right up to them. Joe bent down and **peered** into her

raisin-like face. Two (TINY) eyes stared back at him. It

was **ANNA**. Everyone knew Anna, she was always in the

TEMPLE serving **GOD**; she was **VIRTUALLY**

a part of the furniture. Anna was so **EXCITED** to see Jesus

that she told **anyone** who had ears all about him at

least **3** times, whenever she saw them.

EVENTUALLY

Mary and Joe left the Temple ... and the CITY... and Bethlehem... and walked all the way back home to Nazareth. Ouch! The BLISTERS!

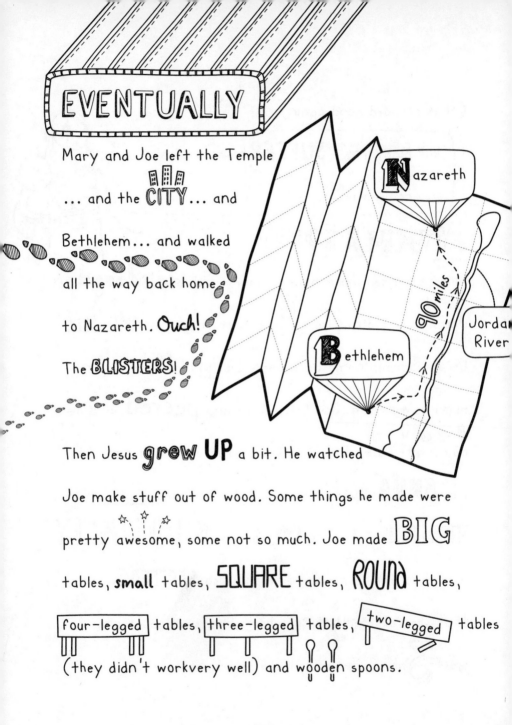

Then Jesus grew UP a bit. He watched Joe make stuff out of wood. Some things he made were pretty awesome, some not so much. Joe made BIG tables, small tables, SQUARE tables, ROUND tables, four-legged tables, three-legged tables, two-legged tables (they didn't work very well) and wooden spoons.

Joe also made QUITE a few WONKY tables, but he turned

those into "SPECIAL SCULPTURES", and told

people they were MEANT to be that way.

AWKWARD.

What KIND of table

would you have made?

But as Jesus got older,

he got stronger and

taller, and smarter

and wiser.

DRAW IT HERE

GOD made sure that he had

everything he needed.

Because Jesus, Mary and Joe were **Jewish**, every year they went back to the **TEMPLE** in Jerusalem to celebrate the **PASSOVER FESTIVAL.** (**WHAT** were they celebrating? Find out more with a **Bible in Exodus 12**.) There were always hundreds of people eating **StRANgE** food and saying lots of prayers. So it was pretty easy for Jesus to disappear among the crowds and, **one year**, when he was about 12, Mary and Joe actually left him **BEHIND**.

Are we nearly there yet?

I need a wee. I really do. NOW!

They didn't even notice that he was missing for a whole day. **MARY** said to **Joe**, "I (thought) he was with you," then **Joe** said to **MARY**, "No, I (thought) he was with you," then **MARY** said to her **friends**, "Is Jesus with you?" and they said, "No, we (thought) he was with you – you should keep your eye on him, you know." And so it went on. AFTER A WHILE, when they **FINALLY** realised that Jesus wasn't with anybody, they decided they should probably go back and look for him. Ooops.

Is it lunchtime yet?

Jerusalem

EVENTUALLY, 3 days later, Mary and Joe found Jesus hanging out in the Temple with all the **TEACHERS** asking loads **????** of questions and saying things that even they didn't <u>understand</u>. He looked completely chilled, and he didn't even seem to have noticed that Mary and Joe had **GONE**. When Mary told him how worried they'd been, and told him they'd **LOOKED** everywhere for him, Jesus said: "Well, why were you looking for me? <u>Obviously</u> I'd be here in the Temple because that's where my **DAD** lives." Everyone stared, and Mary looked at Joe and *whispered*, "What's he talking about? We live in Nazareth."

Mary and Joe kept a **very** close eye on Jesus as they made their way back to Nazareth, for the **second** time.

In fact, Mary kept a **very** close eye on Jesus as he grew **older** and **STRONGER**, and she continued to

WONDER...

NAZARETH

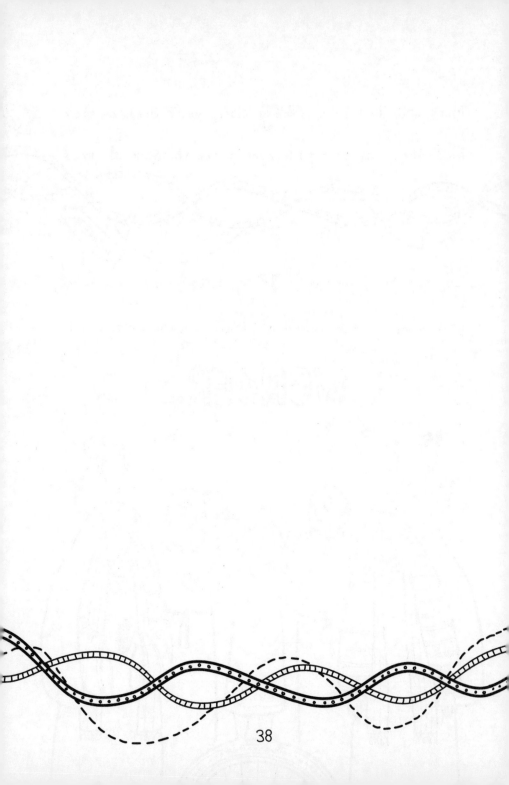

38

CHAPTER 3

DOVES & DUNKERS

So back to the HONEYED-grasshopper guy wearing his

CAMEL-hair coat in the desert...

John had been living out in the desert for quite a while, in fact he'd been there for SO long he'd become an EXPERT, in grasshopper-catching methods. He'd tried lying there waiting for one to JUMP into his mouth, he'd tried sneaking up on them from behind, he'd tried pretending to be a ROCK and waiting to see if they'd LAND on him...

HOW would **YOU** catch a grasshopper? Once you'd **caught** it, what sauce would make it (taste) best? ☐ Ketchup, ☐ Brown Sauce, ☐ Mayo, ☐ Yogurt, ☐ Gravy

One morning John heard a **VOICE**.

It said: Hello, John. I want you to do something for me.

Now if it'd been me, I probably would've thought hearing

voices was a **BAD** thing and I probably really had spent

too long in the desert. But John, he knew <u>better</u>.

He knew it was **GOD'S** voice and that it was perfectly

normal for God to speak to him and give him a **JOB** to

do. John listened to all of God's instructions (which sounded

pretty **WEIRD**) and then did what God had asked.

41

He **wandered** around the desert looking for people.

And when he found them he said, "God wants you **BACK**.

He wants to *forgive* you. Come and be baptised in the

river!" John became **FAMOUS** overnight and hundreds

of people came to see this **crazy** man shouting in

the desert.

Now, you might be **WONDERING** why I'm telling you

this sto ry. It is pretty weird, I know, but you see

the thing is it gets **WEIRDER**... because over **700**

YEARS before all of this happened there was another

man who heard **GOD'S** voice. And here comes the **UBER**

WEIRD bit — everything he said was written down so people

could remember it (you can read *everything* he said if

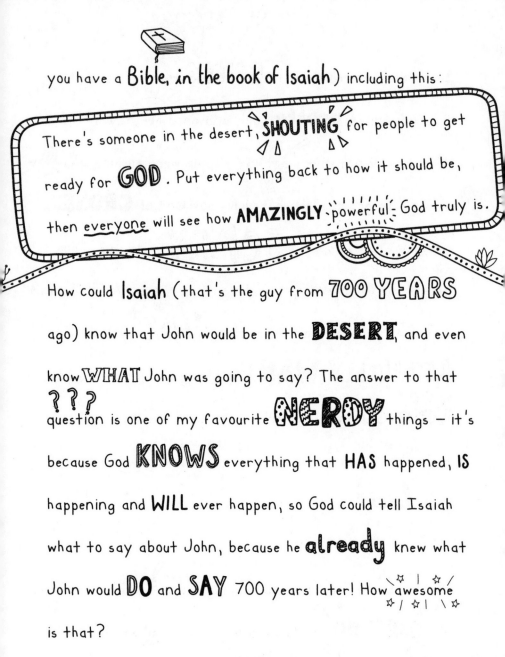

you have a **Bible, *in the book of Isaiah*)** including this :

There's someone in the desert, **SHOUTING** for people to get ready for **GOD** . Put everything back to how it should be, then every<u>one</u> will see how **AMAZINGLY** powerful God truly is.

How could **Isaiah** (that's the guy from **700 YEARS** ago) know that John would be in the **DESERT**, and even know **WHAT** John was going to say? The answer to that **???** question is one of my favourite **NERDY** things — it's because God **KNOWS** everything that **HAS** happened, **IS** happening and **WILL** ever happen, so God could tell Isaiah what to say about John, because he **already** knew what John would **DO** and **SAY** 700 years later! How awesome is that?

Everyone wanted John to **DUNK** them in the river — baptism looked **pretty** cool, and on a hot day in the desert, why not dive right in? People were pushing and shoving to get to John but John got kind of **CROSS**. (Angry John was a bit SCARY!) He said, "You people are **stupid**, you just don't get it do you?! I can't just dunk you and then everything's *FINE*, you have to **ACTUALLY WANT** to change, you have to actually **love** God and want to live for him. That's what baptism is all about, not just getting wet. God will always know if your *heart* isn't right."

People started pushing and shoving **AGAIN**. They were all **SHOUTING** at John all once. They all wanted to know what they were **SUPPOSED** to do so that God would know

they **really** wanted to live for him.

"Well, be **generous**," said John, "if you've got two of

something give one away. And be (kind.) If

people owe you something only take what

you **absolutely** have to. And be happy with

what you've got in **LIFE**, don't always try and get more."

All of a **SUDDEN** everyone went totally silent. They

all stared at John. They starting whispering to each other:

Do you think John might be the (one) who is going to **SAVE** us?

Do you think he's actually telling us a message from God?

Maybe eating grasshoppers isn't **SO** good for your brain...

As usual when lots of people start whispering, it got **LOUDER** and **LOUDER** and **LOUDER** until John interrupted and said: "You still don't get it, do you? I'm **NOT** the Saviour! I'm just here to **baptise** you so that God knows you're serious about him. When the **REAL** Saviour comes he'll be so **AMAZING** you won't believe your eyes.

He's going to change everything. He'll **baptise** you with the Holy Spirit and with fire, and he'll know whether you really mean it!"

The people were a bit **CONFUSED** and thought that being baptised with fire sounded rather painful — and they weren't **SURE** what being baptised in the Holy Spirit meant at all.

(What do you think John was talking about?)

John baptised **SO MANY** people that day that he couldn't remember **WHO** they all were or **WHERE** they came from. **SUDDENLY** Jesus (now a grown-up!) appeared and said with a smile, It's my turn now. Then something happened that John would **NEVER** forget.

47

John **baptised** Jesus. When he lifted Jesus up out of

the river, a *white dove* appeared from NOWHERE

and the voice that John had heard in the desert spoke <u>again</u>.

Except this time it wasn't ONLY John who could hear it.

"JESUS, you're my Son. I'm so pleased with you."

(Did you know the Holy Spirit often appears in lots of different ways in the Bible? Sometimes he's like a **dove**, sometimes like fire, sometimes like wind, sometimes a VOICE, sometimes just a **feeling**...)

After Jesus was baptised he started work. The **REAL** work that he was always *MEANT* to do. He had <u>so</u> much to say and do and he travelled **ALL** around to talk to loads of different people and do lots of proper EPIC things. People who heard him said, "That's Joe's son, isn't it — that carpenter guy with the **WONKY** tables?" And they were kind of right, and kind of wrong, because you see, *although* Joe was indeed **MARRIED** to Mary by now, Jesus was actually the son of someone **much, much, much** greater.

There were some pretty ODD sounding people in Jesus' family tree, IN FACT some of them had PrEtTy inteREStiNG stories themselves. So Joe's dad was Heli, and his dad was Matthat, then there was Levi, Melchi, Jannai and Joseph. And then the names just got WEIRDER and WEIRDER ... Mattathias, Amos, Nahum, Esli, Naggai, Maath, another Mattathias, Semein, Josech and Joda.

(Not the little green guy from Star Wars...).

Then there were 24 more generations of people with SUPER peculiar names and then came DAVID (the one we mentioned earlier with the giant and the pebble), then Jesse, Obed, Boaz, Salmon and Nahshon.

(not a fish)

(not the lots-of-paper sort)

Amminadab · Admin · Arni · Hezron · Perez · another Judah

(nearly got killed by his dad Abraham!) → Isaac · Jacob

then **9** more people with names that sound like they're

made up (except they were **REAL** people!). Then came

ARPHAXAD (totally the coolest name ever),

Shem · Noah (yep — the one that built the boat), Lamech

(who lived to be **969** years old — just imagine → Methuselah

the wrinkles and imagine how long his hair must've been,

unless he'd had a haircut), Enoch · Jared · Mahalaleel

Kenan · Enosh and Seth

And do you know who Seth's dad was? Adam. That's right

—THE **ADAM** who lived with **EVE** in the garden of

Eden. And where did Adam come from?

Well **GOD** made him. So if we went back through all

the names the other way — (Adam) (Seth) (Enosh) (Kenan)

Mahalalalalalalalalaaaaaaaaa... oh that would take forever,

but **basically** you'd get from **GOD**, all the way to

JESUS. Epic. I have to say, I think this sto ry

is getting kind of **EXCITING** now. Just wait 'til I

tell you what happened next.

Oh, and BY THE WAY , if you're **wondering** what

happened to John — well he went on baptising people and

EVENTUALLY people just called him **JOHN** the

BAPTIST. And he went on telling people they weren't
☺ ☺ ☺
living for God and that they needed to change. John just

wanted to do what **GOD** wanted, even if it got him into

TROUBLE, which eventually it did. When John told *Herod* to change his ways, Herod got grumpy and locked him up in jail, which is where he <u>stayed</u> for quite some time...

CHAPTER 4

FASTING, FEVERS & FISH BISCUITS

SO, you remember the white dove and the **VOICE** when Jesus got **DUNKED** in the river? Well the Holy Spirit stayed with Jesus and told him to go hang out in the

phew!

desert for a **WHILE**. But don't worry, he didn't start wearing camel coats or eating insects, he actually didn't eat anything at all. For a whole **40** days. My tummy's "rumbling" just thinking about it. It must be lunchtime **soon**...

DID YOU KNOW:

People sometimes choose not to eat as a way of helping them pray (they sometimes call it 'fasting', and you should **ALWAYS** check with a Doctor before you try it), but **MOST** people normally start with just skipping a meal — not 40 days!

I'm not really **sure** what Jesus did for nearly **6** weeks out there in the **DESERT**, but I do know this. He wasn't °alone.° Jesus had to deal with the devil almost **CONSTANTLY**. The devil was trying to **tempt** Jesus to do the wrong thing. He promised him rewards if did as he asked, but Jesus was **STRONG**, not to mention **clever**. Every time the devil tempted Jesus to do something wrong Jesus used the **BIBLE** to defend himself. Jesus <u>knew</u> that the devil wouldn't be able to win if he used God's words as protection. Eventually, the devil went away and left Jesus alone. He thought there **might** be a better time to come back later.

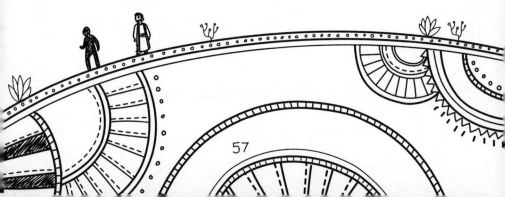

Who is the DEVIL? Everyone thinks he's the little red guy with horns and a pointy tail, but actually the devil used to be an angel, just like the ones we heard about earlier in my story. When the devil was an angel he turned against God and said:

I'm not listening to you!

(with his fingers in his ears and his tongue stuck out, I expect). So God had to CHUCK him out of heaven, and that's when he became the devil. Lots of people are quite SCARED of the devil because they think he has lots of power — they might be right, but I know that Jesus is always more powerful.

Go, Jesus! By the time Jesus got back 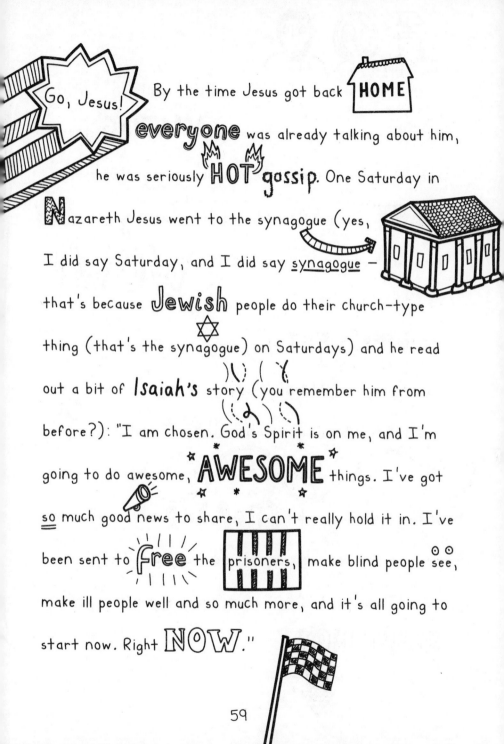 **HOME** **everyone** was already talking about him, he was seriously **HOT** gossip. One Saturday in **N**azareth Jesus went to the synagogue (yes, I did say Saturday, and I did say <u>synagogue</u> — that's because **Jewish** people do their church-type thing (that's the synagogue) on Saturdays) and he read out a bit of **Isaiah's** story (you remember him from before?): "I am chosen. God's Spirit is on me, and I'm going to do awesome, *AWESOME* things. I've got <u>so</u> much good news to share, I can't really hold it in. I've been sent to **free** the **prisoners**, make blind people see, make ill people well and so much more, and it's all going to start now. Right **NOW**."

Everyone stared at Jesus. They didn't quite know what to say. He was saying some pretty **AMAZING** things, even if some of them sounded almost scary. He was the **BEST** teacher they'd heard in a *long* time, and he wasn't even a (TINY) bit boring. **WOW!**

The **WEIRDEST** thing was, even though Jesus was reading some of **Isaiah's** story, he made it sound like he was talking about himself. But **HOW** could he be? Isaiah wrote all that stuff hundreds of years ago. Jesus knew people were a bit **FReAKeD** out by what he'd said, so just to make sure they'd really got it right, he said: "Those words I just read, they're going to come true **RIGHT NOW.**"

People could not stop talking about JESUS, they told all their Friends and Families about him:

He is saying some *pretty* outrageous things.

I mean he's JUST Joe the carpenter's son, right?

Why does he think he's going to make blind people SEE?

That's CRAZY.

Or maybe, just maybe, he might?

THEN, if the things he'd said weren't WEIRD enough already, he said: "NO ONE ever likes the people who bring them God's message, especially when they do it in their own TOWN. In fact, in the PAST, God's messengers reached out to people who didn't even follow him, because those who did just weren't bothered."

Jesus was really pushing it here, and everyone listening to him very quickly went from FReAKeD out to extra ANGRY. So angry, in fact, that they grabbed Jesus and kicked him out of Nazareth and then they chased him like a swarm of angry wasps right to the edge of a cliff. They were getting ready to throw him off the top

when they SUDDENLY couldn't find him. They accused each other of hiding him, they pulled each other's beards to make SURE he wasn't hiding in disguise, but he was nowhere to be found. He really had just disappeared. The crowds wandered off back into town feeling even angrier than before — and now they had **sore** beards

as well. *Gggrrrr....*

Jesus didn't go back to **N**azareth that day, I mean would **YOU**, if you thought someone was going to sling you

off a cliff? No thanks. **INSTEAD** he went to a place

called **C**apernaum (ka-per-knee-um) where people **ACTUALLY**

wanted to *listen* to what he had to say. IN FACT,

while he was there the things he'd said back in Nazareth

really started to **HAPPEN.**

There was a guy who had an evil spirit living in him and

Jesus just chucked it out— **SIMPLE** as that. The people

were absolutely amazed.

(Evil Spirit? SPOOKY. Well not really... In the same way that GOD wants to send his Holy Spirit to come and live in us and do good stuff, sometimes, although really NOT too often, *bad spirits* get there first. But even *if* they manage it, Jesus always has the power to kick them out — just like he did in this story.)

HOW did he do that? What KIND of guy is this? I heard he was just a carpenter's son, that Joe guy who made WONKY tables, but he seems WAY more INTERESTING than that to me.

Pretty soon everyone knew about Jesus for miles

around. He just kept on doing more and more AMAZING things. IN FACT, people actually started to EXPECT him to do amazing things ALL the time. Even after a busy day of being AWESOME, when Jesus turned up at his friend Simon's house he had another job to do. Simon's mother-in-law was really sick, so Jesus ORDERED ➡ her fever to go away, which it did, and then she cooked his dinner! YUM!

Even AFTER he'd eaten his dinner (Simon's mother-in-law was an EPIC cook — fish in fish sauce with fish biscuits. Nom...) people just kept on coming, so Jesus healed them from all sorts of illnesses. He got rid of more EVIL spirits, and the people kept coming — so he kept on being awesome all evening. TIRING work...

Zzzzzzzzzzzzzzzzzzzzzzzzz....

In the morning, Jesus was proper worn out (he was so tired that his face looked like he'd been hit with a saucepan), so he decided to take a walk before everyone else was up. But even then there were people WAITING for him and they FOLLOWED him everywhere — they just wouldn't leave him alone. They wanted more and

more of his awesomeness. Eventually Jesus said: "I know you want me to stay, but if I do then other **PEOPLE** in other **TOWNS** won't get to hear about how great God is, will they? And that's **WHY** I came, to do these **AWESOME** things so people can really see how amazing God is."

FINALY, the people let him go and Jesus **SPREAD** his awesomeness all over the place. Well, all over Judea anyway.

Capernaum

Nazareth

Bethlehem

CHAPTER 5

FLOPPY FISHERMEN & A MAN ON A BLANKET

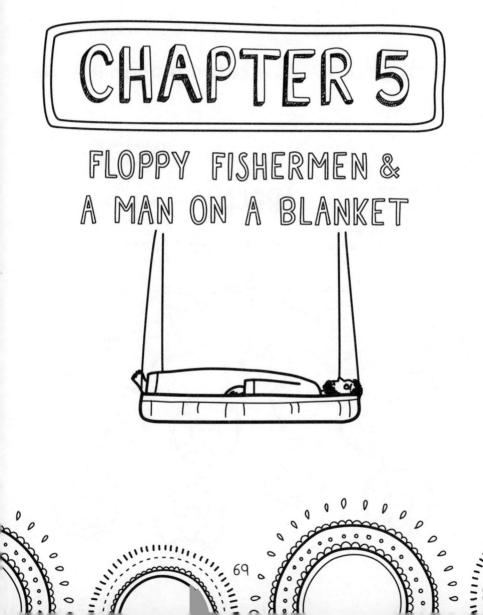

JESUS had a plan. He knew he could carry on spreading his awesomeness by himself, but he also **knew** that it would spread _even_ further if he got a few people to **HELP** him out. Great **team player**, that Jesus.

I expected that Jesus would choose the **BEST** of the **BEST**, the super-**RICH** people, the ones that had the coolest clothes and the biggest houses, but he didn't.

He chose a real bunch of *Flops.*

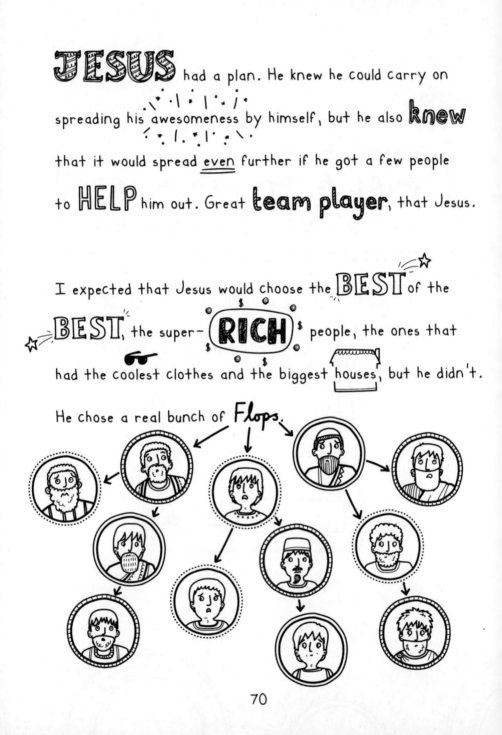

People were still FOLLOWING Jesus everywhere. He had genuine celebrity status and everyone wanted to hear what he had to say. One day Jesus was teaching by Lake Galilee, and there were SO many people pushing to get closer that they almost pushed him in. SO, Jesus climbed into a boat and told Simon, who owned the boat, he fancied a trip out on the lake (Simon was a fisherman, but not a very GOOD one just recently...). Simon pushed off from the shore and then Jesus said, "Stop, that'll do." Simon was CONFUSED.

"But I THOUGHT you wanted to go on a..." he said, but Jesus had seated himself, facing the crowds of people, and carried on speaking to them.

After a while, Jesus turned round and said to Simon, "Right, let's go catch some **FISH**." Simon was even more **CONFUSED**. He'd been out all **night** trying to catch fish and hadn't caught a single one. IN FACT , he was <u>convinced</u> that **ALL** the fish had disappeared. He **normally** caught a few, but this time he'd only managed to drag up the odd **ROCK** and a few **STINKY** old sandals.

Simon looked at Jesus. There was something about his face that seemed **DIFFERENT**. Simon kept staring at Jesus. Eventually Jesus broke the **AWKWARD** silence and said, "Come on Simon, let's go fish. Row out a bit and **sling** out the nets." Simon thought **maybe** Jesus knew where all the fish had GONE — either that or he was playing a not very FUNNY prank. But then, he still had a look on his face that Simon couldn't quite figure out, sort of SERIOUS, sort of happy, sort of a "TRUST me, it's OK" face.

"OK then," said Simon slowly, "tell me where to drop the nets and I'll do it, BOSS."

When Simon came to PULL the nets back up he was totally FLABBERGASTED.

There were SO MANY fish his nets were starting to

rip. As he pulled and pulled Jesus smiled, and they (both) began

to "laugh". But Simon couldn't get the nets into the boat

and, even when he called his fishermen friends over

to help, there were so many fish their boats started to

SINK. Even James and John (pretty GOOD

fishermen!) had NEVER seen this many fish in one

place before. It was AMAZING! Did Jesus

have a special fish radar, or something? When the fish

just kept on piling into the boat, Simon SUDDENLY

realised what had just happened. He began, slowly, to put

all the PIECES together in his head:

So, Jesus had done all this cool stuff...

People were following him everywhere...

Jesus was in (his) boat...

Jesus had just given him the biggest catch of fish he'd ever seen...

WOAH... maybe, Jesus was actually...

Simon FELL on his knees and mumbled, "Jesus don't come near me, I'm a BAD man, I've done BAD things, I'm not good enough for you, you're just too AWESOME."

"Simon, don't WORRY — you're a wonderful fisherman, in fact you ALL are. Except you're not going to catch FISH any more, you're going to catch PEOPLE."

Simon was CONFUSED as usual, and his mates didn't really know what Jesus meant, but they were convinced it could only be something GOOD.

So they pulled in their boats, left the FISH, the

NETS, the OARS and everything behind, and they

RAN after Jesus.

Jesus ended up in a local TOWN and people were following

him everywhere again, and while he was walking along

a man ran to up him and knelt down at his feet. This man

had a HORRIBLE skin disease. All his skin was

falling off and he looked all Lumpy and bumpy.

Ewww...

Everyone always AVOIDED people like him; they didn't

want to catch their germs and they were always asking

for money. But Jesus didn't avoid him. Jesus stopped

and looked him in the eye.

You can **FIX** me Jesus, I know you can, if you want to; you have the power to make me better.

Of **COURSE** I want to — you're healed. That's it.

The man's skin **IMMEDIATELY** looked fresh and **NEW**, he didn't even have any scars. All the lumpy, bumpy bits were gone. He was so **happy**, he couldn't wait to tell everyone, but just as he turned to leave Jesus said, "**Don't** tell anyone what happened, just **POP** along and see a priest and then people won't **have** to avoid you any more because they'll **SEE** that you're well."

Don't tell anyone? That's **crazy**! Jesus just did something **SUPER AWESOME** and he doesn't want anyone to know? **WEIRD**. Why would he do that?

WHY do you think Jesus <u>didn't</u> want the man to tell anyone what had happened?

Jesus kept on meeting people, talking to them, teaching them, healing them, eating with them and just generally being **AMAZING**.

But, Jesus always made sure he took some **TIME** out.

He often disappeared off on his own just so that he could talk to God and listen to what he **might** have to say.

WHY do you think Jesus needed some time out? (What) kinds of things do you DO to take time out? When could you take some time out to talk to God and listen to what he might want to say to YOU?

AFTER A WHILE, the news about Jesus spread to the Pharisees and their friends in the area. When they heard what JESUS was doing and saying they were very suspicious of him. They didn't LIKE the fact that Jesus was stirring up the people, getting them EXCITED, and causing CHAOS. They decided they'd have to see for themselves what all the fuss was about.

So they chose a day and ALL went to find Jesus and check him out.

DID YOU KNOW:

The "Pharisees" were a group of people who were **ABSOLUTELY** obsessed with God's laws. They made sure that **everyone** followed the laws to the letter. IN FACT they (actually) took things a bit **TOO** far... keep reading to find out what Jesus said to them.

They travelled for **miles** and **miles** just to see what Jesus was **up** to. When they arrived they saw that what people had been saying was **TRUE**, but they also saw something they really didn't expect.

As usual, everyone was **CROWDING** around Jesus, shouting about their "SORE" elbows, dodgy knees and **manky** skin. They knew Jesus could **HEAL** them and they just wouldn't GO AWAY! Jesus couldn't get out of the house he was in because there were so many people PUSHING to get in at the door.

Some people were carrying a man on a blanket, because he couldn't walk. They wanted Jesus to heal him, but they couldn't get through the CROWD, let alone through the door. Then one of them had an idea. "We can't go under the crowd, we can't go round the crowd, we can't go through the crowd... so... let's go over them." He CLIMBED up on to the ROOF of the house and started pulling off the tiles until he'd made a HUGE hole!

I mean, imagine if that's your roof — some random people just arrive and start PULLING bits off!

Everyone inside stared up at him. Then, a bulging blanket began to come down *slowly* through the hole. When the blanket **FINALLY** arrived on the floor, it unfolded to reveal a man lying there. He couldn't move and hadn't been able to move for **YEARS**. Lots of people looked at Jesus to see how he'd react, but he simply **smiled** and said, "My friend, your **SINS** are **FORGIVEN**." What a strange thing to say. Why didn't he just say, "You're healed", or something?

WHAT IS SIN? Christians talk about sin all the time. Maybe **too** much of the time, actually... But what even **IS** it? Basically, sin is just a *fancy* word for saying "not loving God properly". A sin is a thought, an action, a WORD, or anything that we do that GOD wouldn't want. The TROUBLE with sin is that it gets in the way of a GOOD relationship with God, because God really doesn't like sin. But the GREAT thing is that he DOES love us and so he WANTS to FORGIVE us and start over.)

When the PHARISEES and temple geeks heard Jesus say, "Your sins are forgiven", they got pretty MAD.

Who does he think he is?

He's breaking all the rules.

ONLY GOD can forgive sins — he's just old Joe's boy from Nazareth.

But Jesus **STOOD** his ground and said, "**WHY** do you think I'm breaking all the rules? What's easier? Telling this man he's **FORGIVEN**, or telling him he's **HEALED**? The Son of Man has the *right* to forgive sins."

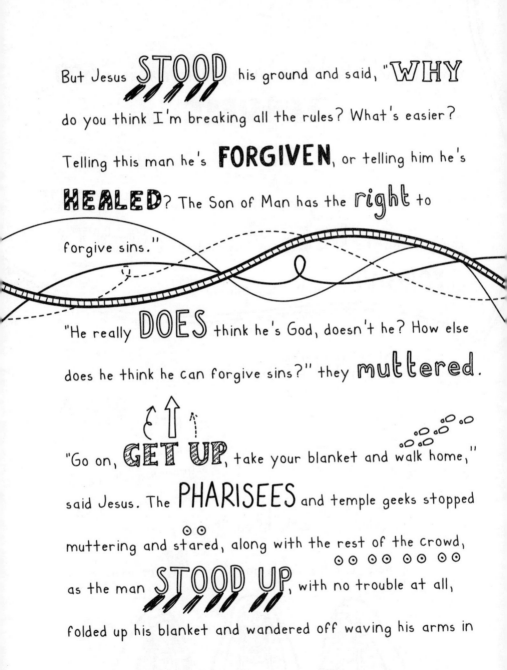

"He really **DOES** think he's God, doesn't he? How else does he think he can forgive sins?" they **muttered**.

"Go on, **GET UP**, take your blanket and walk home," said Jesus. The **PHARISEES** and temple geeks stopped muttering and stared, along with the rest of the crowd, as the man **STOOD UP**, with no trouble at all, folded up his blanket and wandered off waving his arms in the air and shouting about how **AMAZING** God is.

Even though **everyone** knew Jesus was healing people,
they also knew he was saying **INCREDIBLE** things
about himself. They knew he was *PUSHING* it
with the **PHARISEES** and temple geeks, but they just
couldn't stop being amazed **every single time.**

Later on, when the crowds had eventually died down, Jesus went out for a walk. It didn't take **long** before he saw another **CROWD** of people — except this time they weren't queuing to get a glimpse of him. They were **ACTUALLY** queuing to pay their taxes. They **HATED** paying their taxes, but they **HATED** the tax collectors even more. Tax collectors were always *stealing*, **cheating** and **LYING** their way into getting more money off people. They always took **more** than they were **SUPPOSED** to, and there was nothing anyone could do.

Jesus *PUSHED* in, right to the front of the queue, and said to the tax collector (his name was Levi),

Come with me — and he did! Levi got up and left ALL the taxes and ALL his extra cash right there and walked off with Jesus.

Levi took Jesus back to his **HOUSE** and threw a

Massive Party

They had **loads** of food and Levi invited all his tax collector mates and their friends round, too. ☺ ☺ ☺ ☺

The PHARISEES and the temple geeks were still hanging around, spying on Jesus. They were getting pretty grumpy now, too.

Not only does the guy think he's God, but he's hanging around with scumbags — lying, cheating, thieving scumbags.

Jesus heard the Pharisees GRUMBLING outside, came

out and said to them: "You don't GET it, do you? If

you're well, you don't need a Doctor, if you're ill, then

you do. I didn't come here to hang out with all the nice

people and tell them all about GOD, I came to save

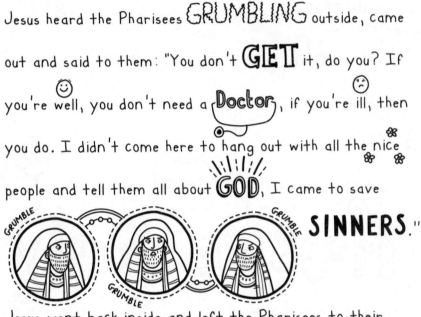

SINNERS."

Jesus went back inside and left the Pharisees to their

GRUMBLES. GRRR.

Everyone was enjoying the party — eating, drinking,

talking, laughing, dancing, more eating... nom nom nom

HA HA HA

A few people came to Jesus and said, "We've heard

that your followers **NEVER** go without food or drink

– John's followers (yep – that's hairy locust John from

earlier) do, to help them pray – so why don't yours?"

Jesus told them that his followers didn't need to go without

food and drink while he was **still** around, but one day

he **WOULDN'T** be around any more – and :then: his followers

would sometimes stop eating and drinking to help them pray.

The people thought it was a bit **ODD** for Jesus to be

talking about him "not being around" – he was **young**,

FIT, healthy, popular (well, mostly!) – so it'd be years

before he wasn't around any more. They were about to go

BACK to the party when Jesus spoke again:

"If you've got OLD clothes you don't cut up NEW fabric to patch them up. The new fabric would need time to Shrink before you used it, so it just wouldn't work with the old material — it'd just make the holes even worse. If you've got OLD wineskins, you wouldn't put NEW wine in them — they'd BURST and you'd waste all your wine. You'd put new wine in new wineskins, wouldn't you? People think old wine is BEST, but they forget that the new wine will be even better in the end."

(Wineskins? What is JESUS on about? 2,000 years ago people didn't have wine bottles, they just had these leather pouches to store their wine in. They worked well for a WHILE, but wine made them stretch and then eventually they'd burst.)

The people thought Jesus was talking in **RIDDLES**: they weren't **really** sure what he meant, but they wanted to know. They knew  clothes and wineskins, and they really liked old wine, but maybe Jesus was on to something. Why was he **SO CONVINCED** that the new wine would be better?

(Jesus often used stories and pictures to get his point across because he wanted people to understand what he was saying. **Sometimes** they didn't get it, though, and even today we have to really think about it to *figure* out what he meant. What do **YOU** think Jesus was getting at?)

CHAPTER 6

BATHS, BLESSINGS & BUILDERS

Jewish people have a SABBATH every week. No, it's not a special kind of bath, it's really just a day when everyone gets to have a rest — which is really *nice* —

IN FACT you might ACTUALLY take a bath on the Sabbath — but only if you didn't carry any water — so you'd have to go to a pool or something — but then you might walk too far — oh, it's all so COMPLICATED!

(The Sabbath — or the Jewish REST day — was something that GOD had told his people to do since the beginning of time. Every 7th day everyone was supposed to take a break, spend some time resting and spend some time with God.

As usual, the PHARISEES and temple geeks took this idea just a little bit TOO FAR and came up with all kinds of RIDICULOUS rules about what counted as work and what didn't... they totally missed the point ...)

One Sabbath day, Jesus and his mates were just hanging out in a field of wheat, relaxing, chatting and pulling up the ODD wheat stalk or two. They were getting quite "hungry" and so picked the chewy bits off the wheat and had a nibble. Some PHARISEES were watching them and pounced on them straight away. "It's the Sabbath, you know, you can't pull up wheat stalks and eat what you like — that's work — it's not allowed — you shouldn't — God won't like that — you're not supposed to work on the Sabbath."

Jesus looked at the Pharisees and said, "My mates are "hungry". They're not working, they're eating. Don't you remember when David (that's KING DAVID – as in killed-a-giant-with-a-pebble dude) and his followers were hungry — they went and took food that was meant

for something SPECIAL. David ate what he

NEEDED and SHARED it around."

The Pharisees stared at Jesus with their eyes wide open — they couldn't BELIEVE his cheek! He didn't seem

to have ANY respect for their VERY important laws

AT ALL. And then he said: "The SON OF MAN

is in charge of the Sabbath," as if somehow

he had the authority to make his own rules! How DARE he!

A few weeks later, on another Sabbath day, Jesus was teaching a group of people about God when a man with a **WEIRD** hand came to the front. His hand was sort of **SQUASHED** and a FUNNY shape and he didn't seem to be able to use his fingers.

The Pharisees, as usual, were standing at the back, watching Jesus, **waiting** to see what he'd do. If Jesus healed the man then that would DEFINITELY count as work — and work on a Sabbath day wasn't allowed — it was **naughty**, God wouldn't like it. Working on a Sabbath was just not OK. They couldn't wait for Jesus to heal the man's hand, because they wanted to **PROVE** that he was breaking the LAW and make sure he paid the price.

Even though the Pharisees were at the BACK of the crowd, Jesus **knew** what they were thinking (he's *pretty good* at reading minds, is Jesus). So he deliberately made sure **everyone** could see the man with the weird hand and said: "On a rest day should we do **GOOD** things or **BAD** things? Should we save lives or kill people?"

Everyone stared at Jesus thinking, "**WHY** is he asking such **stupid** questions with obvious answers? Of course we should do good things and try to look after people — not **JUST** on a Sabbath day but on every day, all the time."

As they **watched**, Jesus told the man to hold his hand out, and as he did so his hand was completely **FIXED**.

yay!

It looked just like a normal hand, not SQUASHED, not a

FUNNY shape and he was definitely moving all his fingers now.

The Pharisees got really ANGRY this time. They didn't

know how to stop Jesus breaking all the rules.

At that point Jesus decided it was time

to get away for a while. IN FACT, he went off on

his own up a mountain and spent the whole night there under

the stars. He didn't even take a tent or any toilet

roll. He just went because he really needed a space

to chat to God. He spent loads of time in prayer, chatting

with Dad (the one in HEAVEN, not Joe) about everything

that had happened and about what might happen next.

In the morning he got his mates back together and chose **12** of them to be his "APOSTLES". (Basically, loads of people followed Jesus around and listened to what he said, but Jesus chose these guys to really **learn** from him. He wanted to teach them about **GOD**, about life, about **HEAVEN**, about all sorts of things really — but he also wanted to prepare them to tell others about him in the *FUTURE*.)

DID YOU KNOW:

The word **APOSTLE** means "someone who is **SENT OUT**"? That's exactly what Jesus wanted to prepare these 12 guys to do... he wanted to send them out on a **MISSION** for him.

ANYWAY, this was who he chose:

Simon (except Jesus renamed him Peter).

Andrew (he was Simon's, I mean Peter's, brother).

James, John, Philip, Bartholomew, Matthew, Thomas and another James.

Then there was Simon (not the Peter Simon, another one), and finally Judas whose dad was called James and then another Judas.

SO, after Jesus had chosen his **12** apostles, they all trekked back down the mountain to be greeted by enormous **CROWDS** of people. There were hundreds and hundreds of them. People had come from all over the place to listen to Jesus and get **HEALED**. Everyone was *PUSHING* and *SHOVING* to get close to Jesus (this was pretty standard by now) because they knew he had real healing **POWER**.

Ow! You're standing on my foot - get off me - there's poo on your shoe!

Get out of my way! I want to see Jesus!

Oi! Move, I can't see, your heads are too big!

Jesus looked around at the huge crowds and decided that **NOW** would be a good opportunity for a bit of a **SPEECH**.

He **cleared** his voice and began:

achem!

"God really wants to **BLESS** you, especially if you're **poor**. He says everything that's <u>his</u> is <u>yours</u>. He **really** wants to **bless** you if you're hungry, too — he'll give you **ALL** the food you need. If you're **SAD**, God wants to **bless** you too; he's got a thousand smiles he's waiting to pour out on your head. If other people **HATE** you and avoid you, God wants to give you **GOOD** things. If people are rude to you and call you names just because you follow me, God wants to **bless** you too! When tough things happen to you, don't be sad, God wants to bless you with really good things — even if you might have to **wait** until you get to **HEAVEN** to have them all!

"If you're **RICH**, though, and you're greedy and life is easy for you, then you'd better watch out. If you get what you **want**, no matter who gets **hurt** along the way, then you should know that it won't **last**. God will make **SURE** of it.

"Do you have enemies? Do you **HATE** them? Well, don't hate them — **love** them!

"If people say **HORRIBLE** things to you, ask God to **bless** them. If people are harsh with you, then pray for them. If someone wants to take your coat, then let him have your shirt too. If someone asks, always give and don't ask for it back. **IN FACT**, if you think about it,

it's SIMPLE – how would you like to be treated? Then be like that with everyone.

"It's easy to be nice to people who are nice to you – why would God think that's an ACHIEVEMENT? It's easy to give things to people if you think they're going to give them back – that's not much of a (challenge,) is it? No, if you really love God then be different. Really love your enemies; God loves them, you know. He has good things for everyone, even the people you DON'T LIKE! And let's face it, you're not PERFECT either – and God still LOVES YOU!

"It's not up to YOU to decide if someone is good or bad, unless you want the same thing to happen to you. Go *easy* on people and God will go *easy* on you. Forgive others when they do something wrong, and God will forgive you. SELFISHNESS just isn't God's way — he's a giver. When you give anything at all for him, he's right back at you with more than you could ever imagine. God's watching, you know — he can see what you're like with other people — and that's how he'll be with you."

Jesus had been talking for a QUITE A WHILE now, but everyone was really listening. He was saying some pretty AWESOME things — but they sounded super HARD to actually do. I mean, seriously, if someone takes your coat — wouldn't you want to keep your shirt?? He really wanted people who followed him to be DIFFERENT.

Then he said:

"If you can't SEE, you can't really help someone else who can't see to find their way around, <u>can you</u>? You'd end up falling down a hole! If you're still a beginner, you can't be <u>better</u> than an EXPERT, can you? It takes time to become an expert yourself.

"It's really easy to tell other people what's wrong with them, but it's MUCH HARDER to notice what's wrong with you.

"First, you should think about how you need to change for the **BETTER** before you tell other people how they need to be different."

"People are a bit like trees. If they're **GOOD** on the inside, then their fruit is good, too, but if they're **BAD** on the inside, their fruit will **ALWAYS** be bad. With trees you can tell if they're good or not by the way their fruit tastes. People are just the same. You can **ALWAYS** tell by what someone says and does what they're really like on the inside.

"I don't understand WHY you all keep saying that you

follow me, but then you don't do what I say. If you do

what I say it's like building your HOUSE on really good

foundations — no matter what comes your house will be

safe and STRONG. But if you listen to me and

then don't do what I say it's like building a house without

any foundations. As SOON as there are floods, as

soon as anything difficult comes your way, it all comes

TUMBLING down."

I don't know about you, but **I** want a safe house. I want to build my life on good foundations. I want to live like Jesus says. It's going to be a challenge — but I know it'll be worth it in the **END**...

CHAPTER 7

SERVANTS, SICKNESS & SMELLS

AFTER his EPIC speech near Lake Galilee, Jesus went off to Capernaum again. Quite a few Roman soldiers lived in Capernaum with their families and servants, and most people really didn't like them.

But, there was ONE Roman officer who wasn't quite like the rest. He had a servant who was really, really SICK In fact, his servant was probably going to die pretty quickly if nothing changed. This Roman officer (I'm going to call him Jim because I can't remember his proper Roman name) cared about his servant and he was prepared to do ANYTHING to get him well again.

Another thing that made Jim

DIFFERENT was that he actually cared about the local **Jewish** people. He knew their names and he understood what was _important_ to them. He tried to **HELP** them where he could.

Jim had heard all about **JESUS** and he asked some of his Jewish friends to go and find Jesus and ask him to come and heal his servant. So, when they found him, Jesus went with Jim's friends, and when he was nearly there Jim sent some people out to meet him with a message.

"Don't come all the way to my **HOUSE**, Jesus, I'm nowhere **NEAR** good enough to have you in my house. But I know that if you just _say so_ then my servant will be better again."

Jesus was SERIOUSLY impressed. "I've never seen someone with this much *faith* — and he's a Roman!" Everyone looked at Jesus, waiting for him to say something else, but he didn't. AWKWARD.

Jim's friends went BACK to his house and the servant was up and about — looking BETTER than ever! He didn't look anywhere near dead!

Jesus stayed on the road, with a huge CROWD following him, and eventually came to a town called Nain.

Capernaum

Nain

Nain had a big gate on

the edge of the town — the **OFFICIAL** entrance ...

⇦ ⇨

where people came and went ... where bodies were carried

out... Hold on a minute, **BODIES**?! Well that's what

Jesus saw.

A **HUGE** crowd of people were carrying the body of

a *young* boy; and his mum, who was clearly **SUPER**

upset, was among the crowd. She felt like she'd lost everything.

Her husband had died, and now her son was *gone* too.

Jesus saw how **upset** she was and he wanted to help her.

Don't cry, he said. Everyone went quiet. Then Jesus said,

sssssh!

"GET UP" in a loud voice, and the boy instantly

sat up and started talking to the crowd.

People were **AMAZED** and didn't know what to think — to be honest, they were a bit **FREAKED** out.

> How did he do that?

> He must be a prophet.

> God is here.

> What just happened?

> Praise God!

They couldn't stop talking about him. They told **everyone** they knew, who told everyone they knew, and everyone they knew, and everyone they knew... You get the idea. **ANYWAY.**

I suspect you might be wondering what had happened to our insect-crunching, desert-wandering **JOHN.**

You remember, of course, that John was **STUCK** in

PRISON after he'd upset *Herod* ?

He had people going **to** and **fro** from the prison, telling

him everything that was going on with Jesus and going back

with **QUESTIONS**. John wanted to know (every)

detail; he wanted to know if Jesus was really all he'd hoped.

> John the Baptist told us to come here and ask you. He
> wants to know. Are **YOU** the **ONE?**

> Look around you, said Jesus What do you see?

Jesus was being super **AWESOME** as usual,

and had been healing people, getting rid of **evil** stuff

and making blind people **SEE**.

"**GO** and tell John what you've seen and heard. Blind people can see, deaf people can hear, ill people are **well**, dead people are alive, there is good news here for everyone. God has good things for **ALL** who accept me and the things I do."

Jesus turned to the **CROWD**: "John is a **GOOD** guy. He did everything God asked him to do. He stuck it out in the desert, he ate insects and wore hairy clothes. He had no *fancy* outfit, he was no posh boy from the palace. No, he was a **PROPHET**. He was more than a prophet. God had already **TOLD** you about John. Have you forgotten? God said he would send a messenger, someone who would come **before** me and get things ready."

that's what a prophet is

(If you want to find out more about what Jesus was talking about, grab a **BIBLE** and find the book of Malachi. Check out chapter **3** verse **1**.)

Then Jesus said something that was just a little bit **CONFUSING.**

"There isn't a <u>single</u> person here on earth who is **BETTER**
than John, not even those who think they're really important.
But when *everything* is how God wants it to be, even the
smallest, most **UN**important person will be better than John."

? ? ?

That's **SOOOOOO** weird! How can no one be as good as

John and then John not be as **GREAT** as everyone else?

What do **YOU** think Jesus might be talking about?

DID YOU KNOW:

The word "prophet" that Jesus used to describe John

means "someone who is *really good* at telling

God's **TRUTH** to others". How **COOL** is that?!

Everyone had listened to what God had to say through John, they'd done what **HE** said and they'd let John **baptise** them in the river. Everyone except the **PHARISEES**, that is. They ignored John and wouldn't (let) him baptise them.

Jesus was looking around the crowd; he could see they just **didn't** get it.

"What are you like? You're just like little children **SHOUTING** at each other. No one can **WIN**, can they? John the Baptist followed <u>all</u> the rules and you said, 'John's a **BAD** guy.' And here am I doing things differently and you :still: don't get it. But **maybe** <u>one</u> day you'll see. John and I were both **RIGHT**. You'll be able to tell by what our followers do."

A **WHILE** later, while Jesus was having dinner (yep, even more fish biscuits), a **RANDOM** woman suddenly **BURST** in. She'd heard that Jesus was eating at the home of Simon (he was a Pharisee) and she just <u>knew</u> she **HAD** to see him.

She was woman with an "**INTERESTING**" past. She'd done all sorts of things that she shouldn't have, and everyone <u>knew it</u>. **BEFORE** anyone could stop her, she burst into tears and **RAN** to Jesus. She knelt on the floor and cried and cried. She cried **SO** much that she began to wash Jesus' feet with her **TEARS**, and then she dried them with her hair. Simon watched, eyes wide, mouth (open) like a giant fish.

If Jesus was **ALL** he **SAID** he was then he'd know she was a **BAD** woman — so why was he letting her touch him?

The woman had brought with her a bottle of really expensive perfume. When she'd finished drying Jesus' feet with her hair, she poured the **entire** bottle all over his feet.

(She didn't do this because Jesus had **SUPER** stinky feet, she did it because it showed how much she loved him and thought he was **worth**.)

Jesus looked over at Simon, who was still staring open mouthed.

"**Simon**. Let me **TELL YOU** something."

Simon closed his mouth and tried to **IGNORE** the woman.

"I want you to imagine two people who owe someone **else** money. One of them owes **5 hundred** coins, the other one owes *fifty*. The **RICH** man who loaned them the money knows that <u>neither</u> of them can pay back what they borrowed, so he says, '**Don't** worry about it — you don't owe me <u>anything.</u>' Which one do you think will (like) the rich man more?"

"I **SUPPOSE** the one who owed him more," said Simon, slightly **PUZZLED?**. What did **that** have to do with the soggy-haired, smelly-perfume woman?

"Have you **seen** this woman?" Jesus asked Simon.

"Of **course** I've seen her," thought Simon. "She's poured perfume all over the floor and *RUINED* our dinner party."

"This woman," continued Jesus, "washed my feet with her tears; she's not even stopped **kissing** them and she's poured perfume **ALL** (over) me that she couldn't afford. **YOU** didn't give me **ANY** water to wash my feet with when I arrived. You didn't kiss me and tell me I was **WELCOME**. You didn't even put olive oil on my head."

DID YOU KNOW:

It was the 'done' thing for visitors to be given water to wash their feet with when they arrived at someone's **HOUSE**. Just imagine how dirty their feet would've been after walking around on **dusty** roads in sandals all day.

124

To **SHOW** that someone was welcome you were **SUPPOSED** to kiss them, and if they were someone important you should mark their head with **OIL**, too.

"This woman has done all **SORTS** of things **AGAINST** God, but I'm telling you now, she is forgiven, and that's why she has shown how much she *loves* me."

Jesus turned to the woman and looked her in the eye.

"Your sins are *forgiven*," he said. "Your faith has saved you. God has **SO** much goodness to give you."

The **other** people who'd been invited for dinner thought Jesus was **OUTRAGEOUS**. "He can't just go around saying people are *forgiven*," they **muttered**.

126

CHAPTER 8

SEEDS, STORIES & STORMS

127

By now, Jesus was pretty **FAMOUS**, and people were following him everywhere — they'd travel from **miles** and **miles** away (on foot, too — imagine the **SMELL**! Eurgh) just to get a glimpse of him.

One day, he sat down to tell them a story.

"A farmer went out to scatter some seeds. He threw them **FAR** and **WIDE**. They went everywhere!

"Some landed on the **path** and gave the birds a tasty snack.

"Some landed on **ROCKY** ground and then died because they couldn't get to any water.

128

"Some landed among NASTY, prickly weeds that STRANGLED the seeds to death as they grew.

"But some landed on lovely brown soil and grew up to be TALL and STRONG."

The people who were listening didn't understand what Jesus was talking about. They were quite CONFUSED. Erm...

(What do YOU think he was saying?)

So then Jesus said: "The seeds are like the things that God says.

"Sometimes people hear what God says but then the DEVIL comes along and makes them forget or stops them believing.

"Sometimes people hear what God says and they *like* it, but they don't (let) it make a **DIFFERENCE** in their lives, and if things get difficult for them they don't *listen* to God any more.

"Sometimes people hear what God says and they **want** to *believe* it, but they're too worried about money, happiness and fame, so there is no **SPACE** left for God in their lives.

"But, sometimes, people hear what God says and live their lives by it, they work **HARD** to learn more and grow closer to him."

Then Jesus told a story about a lamp and a jar and a bed.

"Why would you light a lamp in a dark room and then hide it in a jar, or sneak it under your bed? That'd be stupid, wouldn't it? You'd put it on a stand or hold it up high so that **everyone** who came in would be able to see.

"You see, you can't **HIDE** anything from God. He knows everything; he _even_ knows what you're thinking right now! Listen carefully to what he says and you'll do well."

Then **MARY** (Jesus' mum) turned up with a few of his brothers. But she couldn't get anywhere **NEAR** him because of all the *swarming* people. (**Annoying**!) **EVENTUALLY** Jesus heard that they were trying to get to see him, but he said something rather **ODD**:

"My FAMILY is made up of people who listen to what God says and put it into practice."

What do YOU think he was talking about? _____

_____

People were quite often CONFUSED by some of the things Jesus said. Is he saying family isn't important? Or is he saying family is really important? Or is he saying that actually everyone is his family if they love God?

A few days later Jesus decided he wanted to cross Lake Galilee and, since quite a few of his mates had been fishermen, they didn't mind AT ALL. But, they'd not been in the boat long when Jesus decided to take a nap.

Zzzzzzz...

While Jesus was **SNOOZING** everything went ~~dark~~. The wind was howling and the boat started to fill with water.

Zzzzzzzzzz... Who *sleeps* through a storm like that?

His mates "**SHOOK**" him awake — "We're going to die! **HELP!**" "Oi! Jesus — wake up!"

Jesus opened his eyes, *stretched* and stood up. He looked around at the (storm) and said, "**STOP**, waves, **STOP**, wind," and then sat back down again as the waves and wind **calmed** down.

Everyone stared at Jesus. He stared back. Then he said, "Haven't you got **ANY** *faith*?"

133

"He just told the *wind* and the /water/ to **STOP**," they said to one another, "and they **DID** what he said?!"

A LITTLE **while later** they arrived on the other side of the lake at a place called **G**erasa. Jesus was only just getting out of the boat when a **SCREAMING** man covered in chains fell at his feet. Er — freaky or what?! The disciples kept their *DISTANCE*— this guy looked seriously **WEIRD**, not to mention the fact that he didn't have any clothes on. Majorly **AWKWARD**. Then he said,

Jesus, I know you're **GOD'S SON**, what do you want?

Jesus said, What's your name?

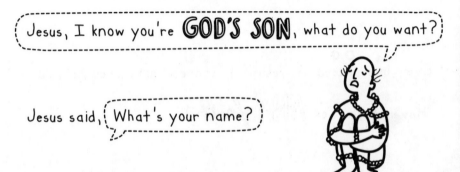

This man had been in a pretty **BAD** place for a long time. He didn't even have a house to live in any more, so he lived in a graveyard. Er... **Creepy**. The people of Gerasa had put chains on him to (stop) him from hurting himself. They all kept away from him, he was super scary.

DO YOU REMEMBER?

We met a man a bit like this guy back in chapter **4**. The man in chapter 4 had an "**evil** spirit" living inside him, and this guy in Gerasa was just the **same**. That's why he had a major reaction to Jesus — the evil spirit inside the man knew that Jesus had the **POWER** to chuck him out...

Anyway. So when Jesus asked what his name was, the man said, **LEGION**.

DID YOU KNOW:

"Legion" (Lee-jun) was the name for a **BIG** group of Roman soldiers. A legion could sometimes include up to (6,000) men!

SO, saying that your name is basically "lots of Roman soldiers" is a bit **ODD**, but if you think about it, it kind of makes **sense**. There wasn't just **ONE** evil spirit living in him, but **lots**, and **lots**, and **lots**...

But you know, it <u>didn't</u> matter to Jesus how many evil spirits there were, because **ALL** he had to do was tell them to **LEAVE**.

JUST BEFORE Jesus told the legion to go, they

spoke to him. "**PLEASE** don't send us to where we'll be

punished," they said, "send us into those pigs over there instead."

And strangely enough, that's exactly what Jesus did.

The pigs **SUDDENLY** rushed down the hill and ran straight

into the lake and drowned. Ewwww.

So why didn't Jesus just get **RID** of the demons and leave

the pigs alone? **WELL...** the short answer is, he knew it wasn't

the right time yet (God would defeat evil in the end) and

for now all he wanted was to heal people and set them free.

The men who had been looking after the pigs couldn't **BELIEVE**

what they'd just seen. They *RAN* into town and told everyone.

NO ONE believed them, so they came to see for themselves.

The very same man they'd left chained in the graveyard

seemed completely NORMAL. He even had clothes (on)

— which was a major improvement! You'd think the people

would've been AMAZED. But actually, they were just

"scared", so they asked Jesus to go AWAY. They were

properly FREAKED out. As Jesus and his mates climbed

back into their boat, they heard, "JESUS, JESUS,

wait for me, I'm coming with you!" It was the man who'd

just been HEALED SPLASHING

his way through the water, trying to climb into the boat.

"No, you're not," smiled Jesus. "Go home, and tell as

MANY people as you can about what God has done for you."

As soon as the opposite shore came into sight they saw a

HUGE CROWD. A man called Jairus was at the front of

the crowd. He was **desperate** to see Jesus. His daughter

was *dying* and he BEGGED Jesus to come and see her.

They **set** off, and the crowds followed.

One of the women in the crowd had been

ill for TWELVE years. She had spent all her

money, and tried every (idea,) but she just kept on bleeding.

It was horrible. Ewwwwww... Jesus was her **last**

resort. She'd heard he could do amazing things, and she

believed he could do amazing things for her. She *PUSHED*

and *PUSHED* her way through the crowd and just managed to

touch the **edge** of Jesus' clothes with the TIP of her finger.

Even though everyone was pushing and shoving all around him, Jesus **KNEW** that someone had just touched his clothes.

He stopped **SUDDENLY** and said, "Who touched me?"

His mates thought he was being a bit **ODD**. "Everyone is *PUSHING* you, what are you on about?"

"No," said Jesus. "Someone touched me. I felt power leave me."

The woman came out from the crowd and **knelt** on the floor in front of Jesus. She *explained*: "I've tried everything — I've been ill for **SO** long, but one touch of Jesus and I'm **HEALED**."

"You're healed because of your *faith*," said Jesus. "Have **PEACE** from God."

MEANWHILE, Jairus had been waiting, worrying what was happening to his daughter. Then his **WORST** fears were realised when he saw someone from his **HOUSE** running towards them.

"She's **DIED**. She's *gone*. Don't bother him any more."

But Jesus said, "**DON'T** worry, Jairus. It's **OK**. Have *faith* and she'll be **well** again." When they arrived at Jairus' house everyone was crying. Great big **soggy** tears and super **LOUD** waily sobs. The little girl really **had** died after all.

Jesus went in with **Peter**, **James**, **John**, Jarius and his wife.

"She's **NOT** dead, she's just **asleep**," said Jesus.

Everyone "**LAUGHED**" at Jesus. They must've

thought he was a little bit stupid — clearly she was very dead!

But then, Jesus **held** the little girl's hand and said, "Get up!"

And right before their eyes she **STOOD** up, alive and well.

Everyone stared. They were **speechless**. Jesus looked

around at them and smiled. "Give her some (food)," he said,

"and don't tell **ANYONE** what has happened here today."

Hasn't he done that before, telling people **NOT** to say what

has happened? I'm **SURE** he (must) have had a really

good reason for it. **Perhaps** we'll find out in a bit...

CHAPTER 9

FEAR, FOOD & FOLLOWERS

The disciples had been FOLLOWING Jesus around for QUITE a while now. They'd seen him heal people, get rid of **evil** spirits, teach people how to live and more besides.

Jesus decided it was their turn. He told them they had God's power over illness and evil spirits. "I want you to go travelling and tell everyone the good news. Don't take anything with you at all, no spare clothes, no bag, no food, no money!" Can you imagine? Only one pair of pants? Ewww.

"When you arrive at a TOWN," he went on, "if people are nice to you and offer you a place to stay, then stay there. If they're NOT nice and don't want you to stay, just leave." Sounds fair to me.

And so they did. Jesus' **12** mates went off with nothing, healing people and telling them **ALL** about Jesus.

You'd think this would be a pretty **AWESOME** thing to do and that **everyone** would want a disciple in their village, but not if you happened to be **Herod**.

People kept telling Herod that **INCREDIBLE** things were happening all over the place. The things he heard set him off wondering: Who was this Jesus guy? Was he **JOHN** the **BAPTIST** who had come back to life? Was he an **ancient** prophet who had come back with another message? Herod decided that he would have to go out and find Jesus, see for himself what all the **FUSS** was about.

A WHILE later, Jesus' mates came back, still in the same pants (ewwww), and EXCITED to tell him all about their travels. They had so much to say. Jesus took them to a little village called Bethsaida, where they could be ALONE

AS USUAL, though, they weren't alone for long. The locals SOON figured out that Jesus was there, and they told their friends, who told their friends, who told their friends, who told their friends...

THOUSANDS and THOUSANDS of people all gathered around. And Jesus, awesome as ever, took his time to speak to them all, and HEALED so many of those who weren't well.

After a while, the disciples started to get STRESSED out. They were "worried" about all these people — they were going to need somewhere to sleep and something to eat. And, actually, their tummies were starting to "rumble", too.

zzzzz

yum!

"We're in the middle of NOWHERE, Jesus, what are we going to DO?"

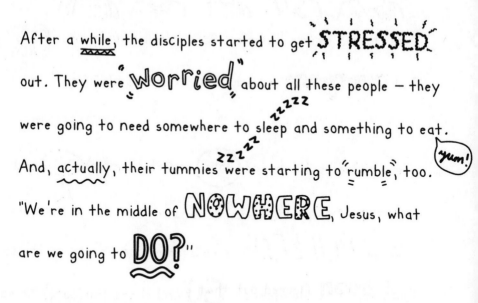

"YOU sort them out," said Jesus.

"But we only have **five** bread rolls and **two** skinny fish. We'd have to spend a FORTUNE just to get a mouthful for each of them."

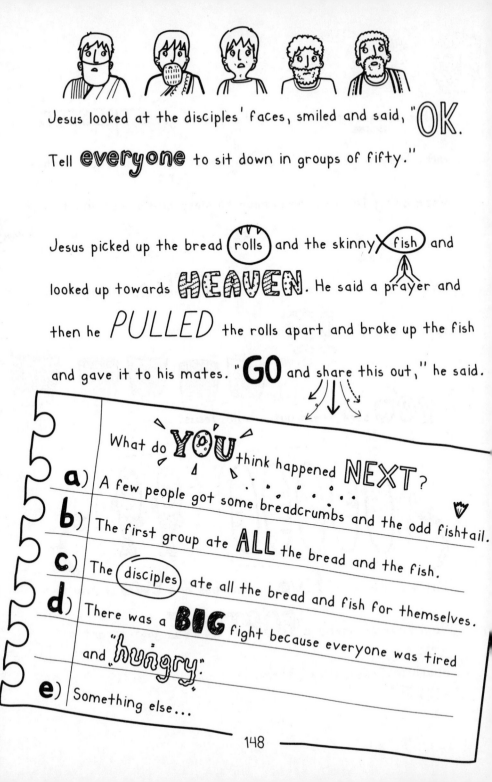

Jesus looked at the disciples' faces, smiled and said, "OK. Tell **everyone** to sit down in groups of fifty."

Jesus picked up the bread (rolls) and the skinny fish and looked up towards HEAVEN. He said a prayer and then he PULLED the rolls apart and broke up the fish and gave it to his mates. "GO and share this out," he said.

What do YOU think happened NEXT?

a) A few people got some breadcrumbs and the odd fishtail.

b) The first group ate ALL the bread and the fish.

c) The (disciples) ate all the bread and fish for themselves.

d) There was a BIG fight because everyone was tired and "hungry".

e) Something else...

The disciples **kept on** handing out food. Every time they thought they'd run out, there was more. The entire crowd ate as **much** as they possibly could, and even then they ended up with 12 baskets of leftovers — and not just **manky** fish bones and bread crumbs, but **PROPER**, tasty leftovers. **WOW**! How did that happen?

A few days later, Jesus was taking some time out. He needed a bit of space so he could chat with his heavenly Dad. Of course, he wasn't alone for **long**, because his mates were just always **FULL** of questions. But today, Jesus had a question for them:

Who do people say I am?

"People say **ALL SORTS** of things. Sometimes they say

you're John the Baptist back from the **dead**, or maybe

a prophet from **HUNDREDS** of years ago."

Who do **YOU** think I am? asked Jesus.

"You're the one who has come to **SAVE** us;

you've been **sent** by **GOD**," said Peter.

"Sssshh... Don't say that to anyone," Jesus replied. "Things

are going to be **DIFFICULT** soon. They have to

be. The leaders here, the **PHARISEES** and the **PRIESTS**,

they're going to hurt the Son of Man. They're going to

KILL him, but **3** days later he'll be alive again."

DID YOU KNOW:

Who is "The Son of Man"? Jesus is talking about *himself* here, but it's **iNteRESting** that he doesn't just say so. When Jesus calls himself "The Son of (God)" he wants people to **remember** that he's not just a human being — he's **100%** God. And when he calls himself "The Son of (Man)" he wants people to **remember** that he's not just God, he's **100%** human too. It's one of the reasons why Jesus is so **SPECIAL**.

"Following me isn't **easy.**

You can't think about yourself all the time, you've got to make sacrifices <u>every day.</u> If you try to **SAVE** yourself, you'll **DESTROY** yourself instead. If you give your life to me, then you'll be {saved.} What do you win if you have everything you've ever wanted, but you've **WASTED** your whole life? If you're not proud of me, then the Son of Man won't be proud of you when he comes back to **JUDGE** you. Some of you, listening to me today, will still be here when God shows up."

Quite a speech. That all sounded *pretty* important, but the disciples still weren't **QUITE** sure what Jesus was talking about. D'oh.

A week or so later, Jesus took **Peter, John** and **James** on a little mountain climbing trip. Jesus was praying, and **PJ & J** were watching him. Jesus seemed to pray and pray and pray. **PJ & J** fell asleep.

SUDDENLY, Jesus changed. His face looked different and his clothes seemed to be GLOWING. Then two more glowing people appeared — Moses and Elijah — it was almost too bright to SEE them. The three of them were talking together about Jesus dying SOON, and what it would all MEAN.

PJ & J woke up with a START. There were three glowing people having a (chat,) right in front of them! Peter scrabbled to his feet and said, "It's GREAT that we're here, let me make you all a little tent so you can stay longer." A tent? That's the best he could come up with? Peter was still blabbering away when everything went very dark.

"This is my Son. The **ONE** I've chosen. Listen to him."

The voice came from **nowhere**. It seemed as if the **SHADOW** itself was speaking. No more words came, and gradually **PJ & J** found they were able to see again.

Except now they could only see (Jesus.) They didn't know what to say, so they just looked at Jesus, and Jesus just looked back. Where did the other two glowmen go?

A day later, Jesus, **PJ & J** came back down the mountain and, guess what? A huge crowd of people were waiting for them.

"**JESUS JESUS**, you've **GOT** to help my only boy. An **EVIL** spirit attacks him and makes him cry and **SHAKE**. Your disciples couldn't make him better."

Jesus looked around at the CROWD and said, "You don't have any faith, do you? How much longer do I need to keep doing this? Bring the boy to me."

As the boy's father PUSHED through the crowd and brought him to Jesus, the boy began to cry and "SHAKE." Jesus spoke to the EVIL spirit and simply said, "STOP." Then he turned to the boy and said, "Be healed."

The boy stopped crying and SHAKING; he was well again. The crowds were AMAZED at what they'd seen. They knew they had seen God's POWER at work.

Jesus called the disciples to one side: "Listen carefully

155

what I'm telling you now is **really** important. The Son of Man will be given to his enemies."

"What's he talking about?" the disciples muttered. "I don't get it."

As the crowds *slowly* thinned out, the disciples started to talk among themselves. IN FACT, they weren't just talking, they were **ARGUING**.

No, I'm **BETTER** than you.

Don't be *ridiculous*, I've always been more awesome.

I'm greatest.

No, I'm the **BEST** of the **BEST** of the **BEST**. So there!

Jesus knew EXACTLY what they were thinking. So,

he walked over to the disciples with a little boy at his side.

"When you look after a child like this, you're looking

after me. When you make me welcome, you make

the one who SENT me welcome. When you put

other people before yourself, that's when you're the greatest."

They all stopped arguing and looked at their sandals.

AWKWARD.

SO John changed the subject. "We saw a man the other

day using YOUR name and saying he could get rid of

EVIL spirits. We told him to STOP because you

didn't give him POWER like you gave us."

"Well **don't** stop him," Jesus said. "If he's not **against** you, then he's **FOR** you." <u>More</u> awkward. Oops.

After a while Jesus decided he wanted to go to **Jerusalem.** So he sent a message ahead to a village on the way so that he'd have somewhere to **STAY.**

BUT when he and his mates arrived, the **Samaritan** people who lived there told him to go **away.** They didn't want him there. Nice.

Go away, Jesus

We don't want you here

LEAVE

DID YOU KNOW:

Samaritans **HATED** Jews. And Jews **HATED** Samaritans. They'd fallen out hundreds of years before, and **never** made friends again. But Jesus didn't care. H loved the Samaritans as much as he **loved** anyone else

James and John got **ANGRY**. They asked Jesus if they should pray for fire to come down from heaven and wipe the village out. "**NO WAY**," said Jesus.

Jesus and his mates went on a bit *further*. AS USUAL, a trail of people snaked along behind. One shouted at Jesus, "I'll follow you ANYWHERE." Jesus stopped and turned to him. "Foxes have their holes and birds have their nests, but the Son of Man has nowhere to call home."

Someone else in the crowd said, "I want to come with you, Jesus, just let me go and check on my family. Then I'm **ALL YOURS**."

Jesus looked **one** by **one** at the faces in the crowd and said: "If you have things to sort out, let OTHERS do that. If you're forever looking BACK, how will you look FORWARD to God's KINGDOM?"

I'm _not_ a fox

I want to follow him!

I have too much work to do

Where's he going **next**?

My hair looks like a birds nest, do you think Jesus would like that?

CHAPTER 10

UNBELIEVING, UNHELPFUL & UNNECESSARY

Jesus wanted the news about himself to spread as FAR and WIDE as possible. So he chose 72 of those who'd started to follow him and gave them a special mission. He said:

I want you to go — go TWO by TWO,
bring in the harvest, it's waiting for you.
So many crops but not enough hands,
ripe for the picking, across every land.
I'm sending you out, like lambs among wolves,
take nothing with you, not even spare shoes.
No money, no bag, and don't say hello,
you don't have the time to greet on the road.
When you enter a HOUSE, say, "God's peace is here,
God wants to bless you, there's nothing to fear."

If peaceful people, God's *blessing* will stay,

if not so 🕊 peaceful, it'll come back **your** way.

STAY there in one house and eat what they give,

don't move around, just stay there and live.

If you're welcome, stay, take *sickness* away,

say, "God's kingdom's **NEAR**— Yes, this [very] day."

But if you're **NOT** liked and they say, "Get lost",

shake dust from your feet and don't hide the cost.

Well, Jesus didn't **ACTUALLY** say all this in a super

awesome rhyme — but it helps me to remember what he

said... **hopefully**, it might help you too.

When he'd finished telling them all these things, he said

something else. Something a little bit SCARY.

"God's kingdom is NEAR and he will judge you. Why couldn't

you see what has been happening (around) you? The people

in Tyre and Sidon would have noticed — they'd have

realised and they'd have said SORRY. But you people,

you people from Capernaum, HOW could you not see

— because you've :rejected: it all you'll go down to hell!

Hmmmmmm ... Hell... What exactly IS hell

anyway? Is it even REAL? Isn't Jesus being

a bit intense?

The **Bible** says that there are only two places people go when they die. One is (heaven), and one is (hell). They are both **REAL**. Heaven is where people will live **with** God **forever**. Hell is where people will live **without** God **forever**. Once you're **IN**, there's no way **OUT**. A place without God is like the ultimate worst **NIGHTMARE**. In some ways, it doesn't **really** matter what (heaven) and (hell) look like — but Jesus does give us a few hints... If you have a **Bible** and want to find out more, take a look at: Matthew 7:13,14, Matthew 13:36–43 and John 14:1–4. And maybe **Revelation** 21:1–4 for a **GLIMPSE** of what heaven might really be like.

And no, Jesus isn't being (intense,) he's being **SERIOUS**. He's trying to let people know that their choices really <u>do</u> matter.

SO, just before they left, without any spare pants, Jesus reminded the 72 that if people said "No" to them and turned them away, they were turning away Jesus **himself.** And they were actually saying a great big "**NO**" to the one who sent him. Some time later, the 72 came back and were incredibly excited. They couldn't stand still!

WOW!

It was amazing!

EPIC!

Even "**EVIL**" spirits listened to us when we spoke to them in your name!

I'll **NEVER** forget the things we saw!

Jesus watched them for a while, and then he said: "I saw the devil fall from heaven. I've given you my **POWER** so that evil spirits will obey you — but that's not the end of it — you'll find your names in heaven — what could make you happier?!"

IN FACT, Jesus started to look pretty happy himself.

Actually, it was because of the Holy Spirit that Jesus was (so)

happy; the JOY Jesus was feeling had come from him.

Jesus said: "Dad — you're **AMAZING**. You couldn't

be better. I'm (so) glad you didn't make all of this for the

clever people, but you made it for **everyone**. The ordinary

people. Dad, you've given everything to me, you're the

only one who **really** knows me and I'm the only one who

really knows you. But I really, really want to tell everyone

ALL about you, so that they can **know you too**."

He turned round and looked at the disciples with

his **HAPPY** face.

"You're **SOOOOO** *blessed*, you know. <u>So many</u> people have wanted to see what **YOU** see and hear what **YOU** hear, but they didn't get to see it **OR** hear it."

A while later an important **expert** in Jewish Law (let's call him **Abe**) came to Jesus and asked him a question: "How do I make sure I get **ETERNAL** life?"

"Well, what do the **RULES** say?" said Jesus. "What do **YOU** think they mean?"

"**Love** God with **everything** you are and **love** your neighbour as much as you **love** <u>yourself</u>."

"Spot on," Jesus replied. "Do that, and you'll be **FINE**."

"How do I **know** if someone is my **neighbour**?"

Jesus sat down and began to tell a story.

"There once was a guy travelling from **J**erusalem to **J**ericho.

He was **ATTACKED** by robbers who took everything he had, **BEAT** him up pretty badly and **left** him there.

"A **RELIGIOUS** leader came down the road and saw the guy. He thought he looked a bit dirty and like he might smell a bit whiffy, so he quickly moved to the other side of the road, as far away as **possible** from the messy scene.

"Then someone who worked at the TEMPLE came along. He {thought} the guy looked a bit dodgy, so he walked past, as far away as possible.

"A while later a man from Samaria came along and saw the mess at the side of the road. He immediately went over to help. He didn't care at all if the man was a bit dirty or smelled bad, and that he wasn't looking too good. He bandaged up the cuts and bruises, and then he took the guy to a local inn. He stayed there with him for the night to make sure he was OK, and then, in the morning, he left money behind so that the injured man could stay as long as he needed. He told the innkeeper that if it cost more than the money he'd left he'd happily pay more when he came back."

Jesus stopped talking and looked **Abe** right in the eye.

"**Soooooo** ... ," Jesus said *slowly*. "Was it the **RELIGIOUS** leader, the **TEMPLE** worker or the **S**amaritan who actually behaved like a neighbour?"

The one who showed he cared. ♡

Well done. Go and do the same then.

Jesus and his disciples arrived in a little village and came across the **HOUSE** of a woman called **MARTHA**, who lived with her sister **MARY**. Martha **really** wanted to have Jesus and his mates come and stay in her house, but there was **SO MUCH** to do and sort if she was going to have so many visitors!

Martha set straight to work on **everything** that needed to be done. But Mary just sat down and listened to **JESUS** talking. (Busy busy busy. Clean clean clean. Bake bake bake. My mum was **ALWAYS** like that when we had people over.)

EVENTUALLY Martha got annoyed: "Jesus, aren't you going to tell her to come and **HELP** me? Don't you think it's wrong that Mary's left (me) to do **everything**?!"

"Oh, Martha," smiled Jesus, "there are always **SO** many things to worry about, aren't there? But Mary has got it **SORTED**. She knows what the most (important) thing is to do, and she's doing it."

CHAPTER 11

PRAYER, POWER & PONDERINGS

Jesus prayed. A LOT. He knew it was really important to keep in touch with his Father in heaven.

Not only did he pray a lot, he was really GOOD at it, so one day his mates asked him to teach them.

"Do it like THIS," he said.

"DAD, in heaven, please help us to remember how AWESOME you are. Let what YOU want happen here on earth. Provide for us every day everything that we need and please FORGIVE us when we do wrong. Help us to forgive others who do wrong to us, too, and help us NOT to be lured into things that are NO GOOD."

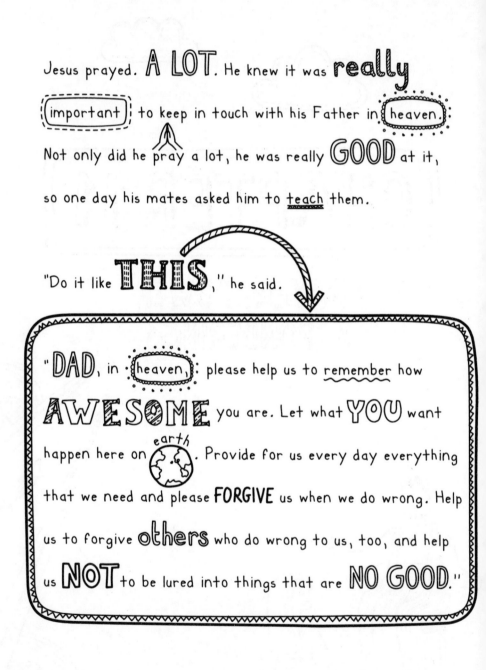

That's a *pretty* awesome prayer. Kind of covers it all really, doesn't it! Then Jesus told another sto ry.

"Imagine, you're about to go to bed, when a friend you haven't seen in AGES turns up. It's awkward, because he **really** wants to come in, but you've got no food to give him and actually you just want to go to sleep but he's **really** "hungry" and he won't go away. I *suppose* you might go over the street and hammer on your neighbour's door, trying to persuade him to help you out.

"**GO AWAY!** he'd probably say. 'We're all in bed, I'm not getting up to give you SNACKS.' But if you keep on asking, he **will** give you what you need, not because he's your **neighbour**, but because you wouldn't go away until you **GOT** what you needed!

"**Ask**, and you'll **get**. Search, and you'll **FIND**. "Knock", and the door will (open.) It's true for everyone. If a kid is **hungry**, what kind of decent dad would give him a snake instead of some fish or a scorpion instead of an (egg?) Even though you're not the best people, you do still know how to look after children. So, **think** about it — your Dad in (heaven) : always wants to give you **GOOD** things. He's ready to give the Holy Spirit to you — just ask!"

People were **STARTING** to realise that Jesus was a {powerful} guy. He kept on healing people and chucking out evil spirits everywhere he went. But a few people started

to get a little bit SUSPiCIOUS. How could

Jesus do these things?

He must be using the DEVIL'S power to get rid of

EVIL spirits. How else could he be doing it?

Show us a sign from God, if that's who you're really from?!

Jesus he turned to face them: "In a place where there is

always fighting, in the end it will always be a GREAT

BIG mess. Families that always fight don't often stay

together. If the devil is doing what you see, why would he get

rid of his OWN EVIL spirits — how would he ever get

ANYWHERE? If I use the devil's power to get

rid of evil spirits, what about those who follow YOUR ways?

What power do they use? If I use GOD'S power to get

rid of them then it proves that God is already here with you.

When an EVIL spirit goes away from someone, it looks

for somewhere else to go. But if it can't find anywhere

then it tries to go back to the person it came from. When

it realises that the person is all FIXED up, it rounds up

a GANG of evil spirits to make itself stronger, and

then it goes back and sets up home again in that person's life.

(This is scary stuff. And that's why it's so

IMPORTANT to know that Jesus has power over

these things. Jesus is reminding the crowd that

it's all well and good to get RID of evil, but

it MUST be replaced with good.)

"If you're not WITH me, then you're AGAINST me. If you're not on my side, then you must be on the other."

SUDDENLY, a woman shouted out from the CROWD, "Jesus, your mum must be really blessed by God."

"Yes. She is!" said Jesus. "But the people who are really, really blessed are the ones who listen to what God says, then get on and DO IT."

"Why do you all keep looking for a sign from God?" Jesus said in a LOUD voice, and everyone suddenly shut up. ssssssh! "The only thing you'll see from God is what Jonah saw. Jonah was a sign to Nineveh, just like the Son of Man is a sign to you."

FACT FILE

NAME: Jonah

FAMILY: Amittai (Father)

AGE: Unknown

LOCATION: Spent some time in a town called Nineveh after he tried to run away to a place called Tarshish

UNUSUAL THING: Once tried to run away from God and spent several nights inside a giant fish. Was then puked up by the fish onto a beach. He probably stank for quite a while! To find out more about Jonah's story, grab a Bible and have a look for a book in it called "Jonah"

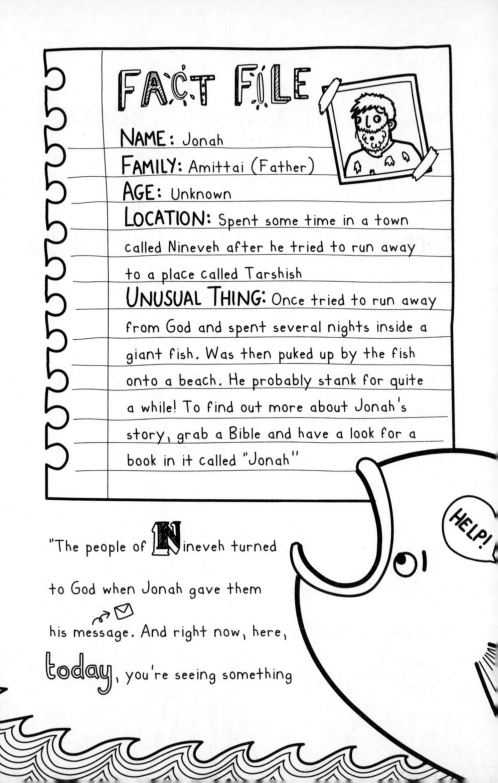

HELP!

"The people of Nineveh turned to God when Jonah gave them his message. And right now, here, today, you're seeing something far more **AWESOME** than Jonah." Then Jesus reminded

the crowds about the whole light under a bowl thing. (You

remember, I'm sure — way back in chapter 8.) But

this time, he added something new: "You see, your eyes are like

LIGHTS for your body. If your eyes are (good,)

you've got the light you need. If not, then the world is going

to look pretty dark. Make sure you stick with the light

and let your light shine everywhere."

DID YOU KNOW:

Jesus describes himself as "The Light of the World"

Interesting... If you have a Bible you can

look this up in John 8:12.

Jesus had been speaking to the crowds for a **long** time.

So when one of the **PHARISEES** invited him to dinner, he went

straight over and sat down for food. Super posh fish biscuits

tonight... **NORMALLY**, people are supposed to wash their

hands before eating, but Jesus didn't bother. The Pharisee

thought this was a bit **ODD** and maybe even a little bit rude.

SO Jesus said to him: "It's not what's on the (outside)

that matters, you know. You people wash all your dishes,

cups, pots and pans, but on the (inside) you're still dirty.

You're greedy and mean. Don't you realise that **GOD** can

see what's on the inside **AS WELL** as what's on

the outside? You think you can get away with just following

the **RULES**, giving a bit of **this** and a bit of

that, but when you CHEAT people the rest of the time and don't even try to love God, it's not like he doesn't notice. You should treat everyone {fairly} and be *kind* to them and give some of what you have back to God. You sit on the FRONT ROW all the time, trying to look good and make sure everyone knows it, but you don't get it, you're not getting anywhere."

The OTHER guests had been staring at Jesus, their frowns getting bigger by the minute.

"Excuse ME," said one of the men who was a teacher of the LAW. "You've just said some pretty MEAN things about us right there."

YOU'RE NO BETTER, said Jesus.

"You tell people they **MUST** do this and they **MUST** do that, but you don't try to (help) them. You talk about God's messengers from <u>hundreds</u> of years ago as if you respected what they said — but it was **YOUR** people who killed them and wouldn't listen.

"God sent those people to you to **TRY** and show you the **right** way to go, to try and show you how **much** he **loved** you. But you killed them. You **ignored** them. You wouldn't listen. Do you really think God won't punish you?

"You teachers of the **LAW**, you know **so much** about God. But you **NEVER** put it into practice, you

NEVER work on your relationship with **HIM** 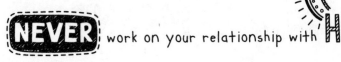 and you stop other people doing the **same**."

Now there was a room ☹☹☹ **FULL** ☹☹☹ of frowns. Everyone was **really annoyed** with what Jesus had said to them. I mean, they'd invited him to ♈ dinner ⌐ — how <u>dare</u> he be so **RUDE**?!

Jesus got up to [go,⟹] but the men were so **CROSS** with him they wouldn't **let** him. They wanted to see if they could make him say something he shouldn't, make him say something that was so obviously **WRONG** just so that they could [catch] him out and get **revenge** on him for pointing out how **NASTY** they were.

Was Jesus **really** being **MEAN?** Why did these men not like what he said? What do **YOU** think he was really saying?

Write your thoughts here

CHAPTER 12

FEAR, FOOLS & FAITHFULNESS

The CROWDS that came to see Jesus and his disciples seemed to be getting bigger and BIGGER. There weren't just hundreds of people now, but thousands. They kept falling over each other and standing on each other's toes, pushing each other out of the way, arguing over who could stand where and WORST of all making that special smell that only thousands of people can make. PONG.

They just wouldn't leave Jesus →alone.← But Jesus wanted to make SURE his mates, his disciples, knew how DANGEROUS the Pharisees were.

"Don't listen to their teaching," he warned them, "it's their way of TRICKING people. They tell people to do (one) thing, but then do something different themselves.

"But even though they think they're doing it in **secret**, ssssshhh...

it **WILL ALL** come out in the end. **GOD** is

the only one you should be afraid of. He has **so much**

more power than people. What can they do after all?

They can only **KILL** you."

Being killed sounds **pretty bad** to me, but Jesus said

something else that would help his disciples to **understand**

"God is in **CONTROL** of your life, he decides whether

you'll end up in **heaven** or **hell,** he has the ultimate power."

Then Jesus asked the disciples to imagine five little birds

being sold for just two (1)(1) pence. "God remembers each

and **every** little bird. God knows even how many hairs

are growing out of your head.

189

"You're worth **SO MUCH** to him, <u>even more</u> than these little birds.

"Do you **tell** people that you follow me? Do you tell them **who** I am?" Jesus asked the crowd, and they suddenly stopped talking. "If you tell **OTHERS** about me, then I will tell **GOD** that you're my followers. But if you | don't | tell others about me, then I **can't** tell God you're my follower, can I? God's {power} is **REAL**. If you say **BAD** things about me, then you can be *forgiven*. But if you say God's {power} <u>isn't</u> real, and if you say that it's actually the **DEVIL** who is doing miracles, then that <u>can't</u> be forgiven. But | don't | worry. If people question you and ask you what you believe, if they **DRAG** you up before the **IMPORTANT, POWERFUL** people, the Holy Spirit will tell you what to say. I promise."

A man "suddenly" **SHOUTED** out above the crowd: "Jesus! Jesus! Tell my brother to give me what he **OWES** me now our father has **GONE**."

DID YOU KNOW:

It was the **TRADITION** for a father to pass **ALL** of his °money° on to his children when he died? People expected the money to be divided / up in the **RIGHT** way, and if it wasn't – it didn't go so well.

"Why should I sort out YOUR fight with YOUR brother?" Jesus replied. "You should be careful — life isn't all about money. Being RICH won't keep you safe. Let me tell you a story.

"Once, there was a FARMER. He was a good farmer, too — his fields gave him so much food he didn't have anywhere to put it. So he thought, 'I know, I'll get rid of my LITTLE barn and build an ENORMOUS barn instead, then I'll be able to keep enough in there to last me forever!' But GOD knows better. He knew that the man would die that night — so what would happen to ALL the stuff in his barn?

"This is exactly what happens if all you care about is getting

more and **more** of everything. Being rich on earth

doesn't make you rich in **GOD'S** view."

The crowd were virtually *silent*. They seemed to have

STOPPED standing on one another's toes and

shoving each other out of the way. For now, anyway. Jesus

had just said some **AMAZING** things — and **some**

of them were pretty challenging too. The disciples were

wondering what he might say next. As if he knew

what they were thinking, Jesus said to them:

"Don't **worry** about your life. There's **NO** point worrying

about what you're having for dinner or what outfit you're

going to wear tomorrow — there are more important things.

What use is **worry**? It doesn't make you feel any better. The birds don't have to **plan** everything and worry about what they'll eat, God just sorts them out. You're **WAY** more important than birds, so **TRUST** in God to sort you out, too. There's <u>so much</u> about your life that you can't *CHANGE*, so don't worry about it. Think about the flowers. They're *beautiful*, but they don't have to work hard to look that way. God makes them *beautiful*, even though they *BLOOM* for just a few days and then they're gone. You're **much** more important than flowers — trust (him) to make you even <u>more beautiful</u>!

"So **STOP** worrying. Only people **without** God worry about these LITTLE things. Put God first and he'll

194

really look after you."

Jesus [paused] and looked round at the disciples' faces. They looked terrified. "Don't be *scared*, little ones. God **wants** to give you good things. Give away what you have and keep your **TREASURE** in heaven. No one can get to it there, it will always be safe. If your treasure is in (heaven), then your (heart) will be there too."

What kinds of treasure do **YOU** think Jesus meant?

Gold and jewels ☐   Lots of money ☐   Lots of food ☐

Things we do on the earth **now** that show that we love God ☐

Hint: It's not gold, jewels, money or food!

Jesus carried on talking. "It's **IMPORTANT** that you're always ready. Imagine you live in a **HOUSE** with servants and you're in charge. You want your servants to **always** be ready when you come home. You want them to open the door as soon as you knock. If the servants are awake and prepared when the master arrives, then they will be rewarded. The master **himself** will serve them and bring them their food, he'll make <u>sure</u> they're well looked after. Being ready matters — you never know what will happen — if you **knew** someone was coming to **BREAK** into your house you'd be awake and ready to stop them, wouldn't you? You don't know when the Son of Man will come, so be **READY**."

196

"Erm... excuse me Jesus," **mumbled** Peter while looking at his sandals. "Are you just talking to us or to **ALL** these people here?"

"WELL", is it **YOU** or all of <u>these</u> people that are like the good servants in my story? Who are the ones that would be **TRUSTED** to do things right without having to be watched? If a servant does a **GOOD** job, then they'll be trusted with more, won't they? If a servant **doesn't** do a good job, then things probably won't go very well. If a servant doesn't do what they've been **ASKED** to do, and does something **else** instead, then they'll get caught out and they <u>won't</u> be trusted any more.

"Servants should be ready to do what they're asked. Always.

"It's the [same] with God, really. If GOD is good to you then he wants you to do good for him in return. Be ready to do what HE wants.

"I didn't come to earth 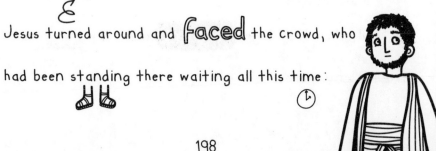 just to be nice, I came to show people a different way. I came to offer them a CHANCE to choose which side they're on. Some will choose ME and some will NOT. Families will be divided when they make their choice."

Jesus turned around and faced the crowd, who had been standing there waiting all this time:

198

"When you look one way and see a big black cloud, you say, 'There's rain on the way,' – then it RAINS. When you look another way and you feel the wind you say, 'HOT weather's coming,' and then it gets hot."

The people were a little CONFUSED. Since when was Jesus a weatherman? Everyone knows you just look at the sky to tell what KIND of weather is coming.

I DON'T LIKE IT WHEN IT'S HOT, IT MAKES ME SMELL BAD.

I DON'T LIKE IT WHEN IT'S WINDY – IT MAKES MY BEARD GET TANGLED.

I DON'T LIKE RAIN, IT MAKES ME WET.

"You can easily tell people about the weather just by looking at what's happening around you... so HOW can you not know what's happening right before your eyes today? Why don't you GET it?

"I'm giving you a CHANCE here, a chance to choose the right thing. Don't miss out. Soon, it'll be too late."

What Jesus was saying to the crowd was SUPER IMPORTANT. He wanted them to realise who he was and to CHANGE their ways. He was trying to tell them that they didn't have to stay as they were, they really could be DIFFeRENT.

The crowd must've been pretty "unsettled" by what Jesus said to them... You'll see WHY soon enough.

CHAPTER 13

TURNING, TREES & TEETH

A LITTLE while later, Jesus heard that Pilate

had killed some people from Galilee because they had broken

the ROMAN'S rules. People wanted to know what

Jesus had to say about this...

(Who is **Pilate**? Well, firstly he's not the flying kind.

Pilate was an interesting guy. You'll hear a lot more

about him as our sto ry unfolds. Basically, he was

a kind of RULER of Judea — a governor to be exact.

He was certainly pretty important and he knew it...)

"Just because Pilate killed these people, do you think they

were extra BAD?" said Jesus. "Do you think they

were WORSE than everyone else? Of course they

weren't. But, remember, if you DON'T change your

ways and come back to God, you'll end up the same way.

"Let me tell you a story." The people all gathered

ROUND to listen.

"Once there was a man who had a fig tree

growing in his fields. It was a pretty useless tree and

hadn't grown ANY figs in three years. So the man told

the gardener to chop down the tree so he could USE the

space to plant something BETTER. But the gardener

wanted to give the tree another chance: 'I'll HELP it out,

really try to look after it this year — maybe it'll do better

next year — and then if it doesn't I'll chop it down,' he said."

Jesus **really** wanted the people to know that, just as in the story of the fig tree, God had ALWAYS wanted to give them another CHANCE to turn back to him. I think I've always been a bit of a useless fig tree, but it's so amazing that God always wants to give me another chance.

A few days later, on the Sabbath (remember chapter 6?), $1+2=3$ Jesus was doing more teaching. He still had more to say! While he was speaking he spotted a TINY person in the CROWD. The closer he looked the more he realised she wasn't TINY at all, she was just bent over and couldn't stand up straight. (She'd been like this for 18 years!) Jesus walked towards her and he called out to her, "You are set FREE!" When he came near to her he put his hands on her and she **SUDDENLY** straightened up. She was actually

pretty **TALL**! She couldn't stop saying *thank you*

to God. "**OO**!" The man in charge of the meeting place was

scowling and pointing at Jesus and came stomping over

towards him. "You can't **HEAL** people on the Sabbath—

that's work," he growled. He looked *pretty* angry and had very

angry looking eyebrows. "There are **SIX** days of the week

when you can be healed, what's **wrong** with all of those days?!"

Jesus turned to face him. "Are you

joking?" he **smiled**. "Wouldn't you take your animals to

the water so they can have a drink on the Sabbath? This

woman is one of **GOD'S** children, she's been unwell for so

long. How is it **wrong** to **HEAL** her on the Sabbath?"

The man, and the other people who didn't **like** Jesus, looked at their feet and said (nothing,) but they definitely carried on frowning. They felt a LITTLE bit ashamed of themselves. But everyone else thought Jesus was **AWESOME**.

"God's **KINGDOM** is wonderful," said Jesus. "It's kind of like when you plant a teeny-weeny mustard seed and it grows into an **ENORMOUS** tree where birds can build their (nests)... It's kind of like when you put a teeny-weeny bit of yeast in some [flour] and then the dough grows to be absolutely **MASSIVE!**"

Jesus kept on teaching people, even when he was travelling. He was on a **journey** to **J**erusalem and people were walking along the road with him. OTHERS came out when he passed through their 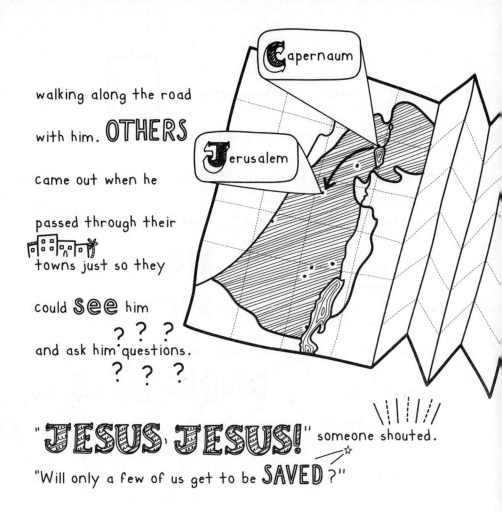 towns just so they could **see** him and ask him questions.

? ? ?
? ? ?

"**JESUS, JESUS!**" someone shouted.

"Will only a few of us get to be **SAVED**?"

"You should do **everything** you can to get through the tiny ⊡ door. Lots of people will **TRY** to get through, but they'll be **TOO LATE**.

"Once the owner of the house locks the door, that's **THAT**. Even if you stand outside and ask to be let in, the owner will say he doesn't **know** you. You'll say 'don't you remember when we had dinner'? or 'we saw you in the street' and he'll still say, '**NO**, I don't **know** you, go away.' Then you'll be **SORRY**. You'll be stuck outside gritting your teeth and you'll be able to see everyone on the inside having a **WONDERFUL** time. This is **GOD'S** kingdom; you've got to turn back to him before it's too late. There'll be people from **everywhere**, **everyone** is welcome, but it's **YOUR** choice. The ones who don't seem special now will be the most special in **GOD'S** kingdom. And the ones who seem special **now** will be the least special."

"Right then, **JESUS**," said one of the PHARISEES who seemed to have **SUDDENLY** appeared. "Your time's up. It's **time** to leave. *Herod's* had enough of you, he wants your head."

Not an especially nice way to greet someone really...

"Well, you can tell that **old fox** that I will keep on getting **RID** of evil spirits and I will keep on healing people until I'm done. And I will still make my way to **J**erusalem because that's where I need to go. ANYWAY, Jerusalem is the place where **GOD'S messengers** always seem to be killed."

The PHARISEES didn't know what to say to that, and they
oo oo oo
watched as Jesus kept on walking.

After a while, Jesus began to look SAD. His face looked <u>miserable</u> and he said, "OH, Jerusalem, Jerusalem, your people have killed God's messengers and failed to listen. I just wanted to protect you like a mother hen with TINY chicks hiding under her wings. But you just wouldn't LET me. And then it will be TOO LATE, you won't see me again for a very long

time. God's HOUSE will be empty and I'll not be back until you say, 'The one who comes in God's name will be blessed.'"

Sniffle. Sniffle. JESUS crying makes me want to cry. He loved everyone <u>so much</u>. Why couldn't they see what was really going on?

CHAPTER 14

EXCUSES, EXCUSES...

It was another SABBATH day. So, guess what happened next?

Jesus was having dinner with a really rather important guy (he was a PHARISEE) and everyone was watching him. Awkward.

SUDDENLY a man with super large legs struggled to his feet.

His legs were all puffy and looked really UNCOMFORTABLE.

He waddled over to Jesus and STOOD in front of him.

He kept on looking down at his legs and then up at Jesus.

Legs. Jesus. Legs. Jesus... Jesus turned around to the other

PHARISEES in the HOUSE and said, "Well now, it's

the SABBATH. So should I HEAL this man?"

They didn't say anything. They just watched.

So Jesus **HEALED** the man and sent him away well.

He could walk <u>normally</u> and his legs looked completely different.

"All of you," Jesus said to the people after the man had

gone, "you wouldn't leave your child in a

well if they fell *in* on the Sabbath would you?

You'd pull them **OUT** right there and then."

HELP!

They still didn't say **anything**. They just looked at

Jesus and pulled <u>awkward</u> faces. What <u>could</u> they say?

Jesus looked around at them **ALL** and <u>noticed</u> how people had

tried to sit in all the best seats, the ones nearest the front,

leaving the second rate seats at the back for other people.

"If you're invited to a wedding party you really <u>shouldn't</u> take the **BEST** seat for yourself. What if someone more important than you is about to arrive? It'd be *pretty* embarrassing if you had to give up your seat because the person who invited you tells you to move. You'd probably end up sat on the f**loor**.

Think about it. If you're invited to a **PARTY** and you start by taking the worst seat then things will only improve. Think how much better you'd feel if you were invited to come and take a **MORE** important seat. If you always try to be more important than other people you'll end up less important. But if you're **humble**, then you'll be honoured."

Jesus turned around to face the RATHER important guy who had invited him to Ydinner P in the first place. He had a few words to say to him, too.

"When you throw a Party don't invite all your mates, your family and the people with all the money. If you do, they'll only invite you round to their place for another party, and then you'll be even. INSTEAD, invite the people who have (nothing,) the ones who are unwell, the ones who could NEVER throw a party for you. There's NO way they would EVER be able to return the favour. But that doesn't matter. GOD will see what you did and bless you in the end." One of the men in the important seats spoke up.

215

He puffed out his chest and spoke in his poshest voice.

"Surely, the best thing EVER would be a seat at the party in GOD'S kingdom."

"Well, let me tell you a story," said Jesus. "After preparing the most WONDERFUL party and inviting LOADS of important people, a master sent a servant to let the guests know it was READY. But everyone kept making excuses. 'Oh (sorry,) erm... I'm busy. I need to try out my new cow.' 'Sorry, I just can't make it, I got married a few weeks ago.' 'I'd love to be there, but I need to clean up the poo in my stable, sorry.'

"When the master heard that people were making excuse

AFTER excuse he said: Right. Go out again and invite everyone. **Anyone**. The poor people, the ill people, invite them (all!) Be as QUICK as you can.'

So the servant went back out and told everyone he could find that they were invited to an incredible party. They couldn't WAIT to be there, but even when they all arrived there was still LOADS of ←space→ for more guests. So the servant was told to go out again, down TINY roads, across fields and across town and to bring everyone he could find. 'I don't want anyone to miss out,' said the master, 'there is so much here to share. But those who made excuses, they'll not get a single BIT.'"Jesus had said all he could. He left the PHARISEE'S house. It was up to THEM now.

217

WALKING, WALKING, WALKING. There was a LOT of walking to do to reach Jerusalem, and the CROWDS following Jesus on this journey grew every day.

Your bum is in my face! Ow!

Listen! Listen - Jesus is going to say something important!

Your elbow is in my eye

As he got a LITTLE bit closer to Jerusalem he stopped and turned to FACE them all. Lots of the people near the back hadn't noticed that he'd stopped, and they all ran

You need a bath!

into each other. "You can't follow me unless you really love me more than anyone. Even more than your family, more than your friends. You can't follow me unless you love me more than your LIFE. You have to carry your own cross and come with me. It won't be easy."

WOW. Just WOW.

"Just imagine for a minute that you're **trying** to build a **TALL** tower. First things first — you are going to need to do a few sums. How **MUCH** is it all going to cost? Have you got the money? If you didn't do that you'd get [halfway] through and then realise you couldn't finish the job. Then what? Well, **everyone** would laugh at you, wouldn't they, and your tower would be *pretty* useless.

"Imagine a **KING** with **10,000** soldiers. If he sees **20,000** soldiers coming for him in the distance, shouldn't he decide if he thinks he can **WIN** before he sends his **10,000** to fight? If he can't win, then he should ask for peace instead. The cost could be **TOO HIGH** if he tried to fight.

YOU SEE, you can't be my disciple unless you're prepared to give away **everything**. I need **ALL** of you."

WOW. <u>Again</u>.

"Take **SALT**. It should be salty, right? If you put it on your food and it's good salt, you can **taste** it. But if it's not **SALTY** it's **useless**, it's not even **GOOD** enough to throw it out with the horse poo! People, if you can hear what I'm saying, then LISTEN!"

CHAPTER 15

SHEEP, PIGS & SANDALS

Everyone **HATED** tax collectors. They always took more money than they were **supposed** to and kept it for themselves. Nobody **liked** sinners very much either.

But not **JESUS**. The tax collectors and **SINNERS** crowded around him to hear what he had to say. And Jesus welcomed them as much as **anyone else**. This made the **PHARISEES** cross. Their angry eyebrows were on show again. "Can you believe it? Now he's (even) eating with people like that. **Eurgh**!" Jesus told them all a story.

"If you had **100** sheep and one went missing, what would you do? You'd leave the **99** in their field and go out to look for the missing one, wouldn't you? When you found it you'd be **SO HAPPY** you'd do a little happy dance with the sheep on your shoulders, and you'd carry it home. IN FACT , you'd be so happy you'd "knock" on **everyone's** doors and invite them to come to an 'I've found my sheep' party!

"It's just like this in heaven ," Jesus went on. "In heaven : when just →one← person turns to God it's as if God throws a **MASSIVE PARTY** to celebrate!"

I don't even like sheep.

I can't dance.

What's he talking about?

Jesus told the **CROWD** a few more sto ries to try to help them to **understand** what he meant.

"Imagine a woman who has ten pieces of silver. One day she loses one. She'd do anything to find it, wouldn't she? She'd look on the floor, on TOP of her things, under her things and in every pocket until she found it. And then, she'd be SO pleased she'd tell all her friends and they'd CELEBRATE together.

"It's just like this in heaven," Jesus said again. "In heaven all the angels absolutely love it when →one← person comes back to GOD.

Yes!

"Or, how about THIS?" Jesus continued. "Imagine a man with two sons, and the younger one asks for the share of his dad's things (which he'd normally not get until

his dad had died). So, the man divides / up (everything) he has between the **younger** son and the **older** son, and the younger son takes his share and **leaves** town.

"The younger son spends **ALL** his money on things that aren't **GOOD** for him, and then he has nothing left. He doesn't even have any money to buy food. Eventually he decides he has to get a job, and he finds a guy out in the country who says he can be his pig shepherd. He is <u>so</u> "hungry" that he thinks even the pig food looks good, but no one gives him **ANY** food of his own.

"When he can hardly **BEAR** it any more he **SUDDENLY** thinks, 'I know, what if I go back to Dad? The people who work for him get nice food — they're not *starving* like **ME!** If I go back and **APOLOGISE** for leaving town and ask if I can work for him, maybe he will let me.'

"So that's what he does. When he is still a *long* way from home he sees his dad on the road running towards him with his arms ← wide open. → When his dad **Finally** reaches him he covers him in (hugs) and kisses — he is so pleased his son is back.

"'Dad, I'm **SO sorry**,' says the son. 'I've turned away from **GOD** and I've turned away from **YOU**. I'm not even good enough to be called your **SON** any more.

'Please just let me work for you like a servant.'

"But his dad won't hear of it and tells his servants to fetch the **POSHEST** clothes, **BEST** jewellery and nicest sandals he has and to put them on his son. And he doesn't (stop) there. He tells the servants to prepare an enormous meal so they can all **CELEBRATE**.

My **SON** had gone, I'd lost him, but now he's back and full of **LIFE** – I couldn't be **HAPPIER!!**

"But, the other son, the one who'd stayed at home and worked **HARD** with his dad, is not at all happy. 'What's all this food and dancing for?'

"'Your brother is **BACK**,' one of the servants tells him. 'Your dad is throwing a **Massive Party** for him!'

"The older brother is so **MAD** that he won't even go inside. Even when his dad comes out and tries to **explain**, he still won't go in. 'It's just not **FAIR**!' he fumes. 'I've worked **HARD** for you for years and you've never thrown a party for **me**. Why should he get a **RIDICULOUS** feast? He left town and went off like an **Idiot**, and now he's back and he stinks of pig poo!'

"'My **SON**,' his dad says *gently*, 'don't you realise you've been with me **ALL** along, and I'm sharing everything I have with you **already**. Your brother was **gone** for so *long*, we all thought he was DEAD.

But now he's back, and he's very much ALIVE!'"

230

CHAPTER 16

LIES, LOOKS & LAZARUS

"**SO**..." said Jesus looking around at the disciples' faces. "Let me tell you another story."

"Once, there was a **VERY RICH** man who owned his own company. He was ⟨**so**⟩ rich that he had a **manager** to run the business for him. One day someone told the rich man that his manager was doing a **BAD** job. [**IN FACT**], he was *WASTING* lots of money.

"**Of course** the rich man asked to see the manager.

"'What have you been doing? Not a **VERY GOOD** job, I hear. You can't **work** for me any more. That's it.' **Byeeeeeeee**.

"The manager was so *upset* that he even started talking to himself. **(AWKWARD.)** 'What am I going to do? I need to *earn* money somehow — I'm too SKINNY to dig, I just can't bring myself to beg... Hold on a minute... I think I have a **PLAN**!'

"**SO**, he went through the rich man's papers and 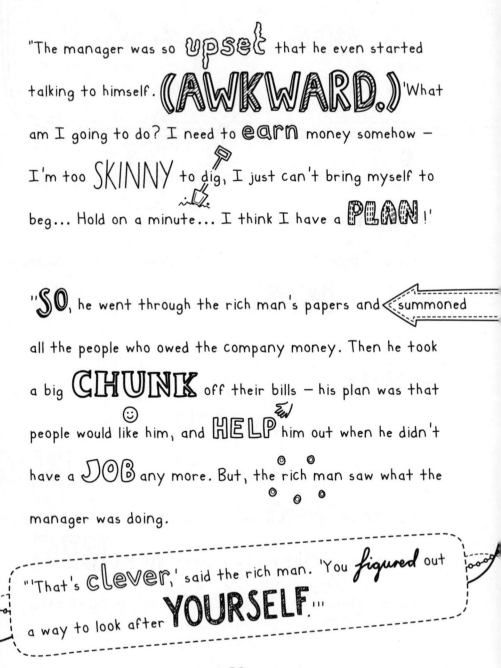 summoned all the people who owed the company money. Then he took a big **CHUNK** off their bills — his plan was that people would like him, and **HELP** him out when he didn't have a **JOB** any more. But, the rich man saw what the manager was doing.

"'That's clever,' said the rich man. 'You *figured* out a way to look after **YOURSELF**.'"

(What an ODD story... CONFUSED? Have a look at what Jesus says next...)

"Listen," said Jesus, "this is what the world is like. People who don't know me look after themselves better than those who do. They're clever, they think about how they can make the MOST of what they've got."

"Do YOU do that?" asked Jesus. "Do you take what you already have and use it WISELY? If you can be trusted with LITTLE things, then you'll be trusted with the BIG things. If you can't be trusted with LITTLE things here on earth, how can you be trusted with the BIG things of heaven? If you can't be trusted with other people's things, then you'll not be given your OWN. But remember, you can't love GOD and love money. You'll always think that one is more important than the other."

(Any clearer? Well, let's just think about it for a minute. We know that JESUS wouldn't tell people to lie, so that's NOT what he's saying. We know that he wouldn't tell people to love money and things more than GOD, so that's not what he's saying either.

Jesus wants his disciples to be who God MADE them to be. He wants them to tell as many people as possible about him and he WANTS God to USE them to do amazing things.

235

He wants them to REALISE that money isn't everything, people are far more important. He wants them to be trustworthy and he wants them to love GOD more than anything else. There. Hope that helps.)

Some of the PHARISEES had been listening to Jesus talking about money and were laughing at him behind his back.

He he

Haha

HA

But Jesus could HEAR what they were saying and said: "All you care about is making yourselves look wonderful. But God sees what's going on inside. All these things that people think are IMPORTANT – they're not IMPORTANT to God.

"Before my cousin John came, everyone had to follow the

Old rules. But now, people have heard about God's kingdom, they've heard how **WONDERFUL** it is and they want to make sure they get a place. But it's not about just following the **RULES**, it's about *loving* God and doing what he would want. You have to be **TOTALLY** committed, just like in a marriage. In a marriage God brings two people **TOGETHER** for ever. You can't just walk away."

The Pharisees were still **LAUGHING** at Jesus, and making fun of the things he was saying.

Jesus just wants to make trouble.

He's just trying to make excuses.

Rules are the BEST.

So, Jesus told one more sto ry. "Imagine a rich man

with super posh clothes and the best extra tasty food.

Now imagine a man who has nothing. Let's call the man

who has nothing Lazarus. When Lazarus was brought

to the RICH man's house, he was given just the

scraps of food that the rich man didn't want.

"When the man who had nothing DIED, the angels came to

take him to heaven to be with Abraham. But when the rich

man died, he didn't end up in heaven. He ended up in hell."

(You remember, Jesus has talked about hell before.

Go back to chapter 10 if you've forgotten!)

(**Abraham** who? If you go all the way back to chapter **3** you'll see that Abraham was the guy who nearly *KILLED* his own son, **Isaac**. Scary stuff, right? He also did lots of really awesome things for God later on... Anyway, when Abraham **died** he went to heaven to be with **GOD**. The rich man would've known all about Abraham and the things that happened to him.)

So, anyway, Jesus carried on...

"When the **RICH** man was stuck in hell, he could see Lazarus looking happy and **chilled** out in heaven. So he **SHOUTED** out to Abraham and said, 'Abraham pleeeeeeeeease can you send Lazarus with some water — it's soooooooo hot down here, I can't **BEAR** it. Pleeeeeeeeeaase?!'

"But Abraham said, '**NO**' and explained to the rich man that piling up **GOOD** things for yourself while you're on earth doesn't automatically mean good things when you die. And having nothing on earth doesn't **AUTOMATICALLY** mean nothing when you die. 'And, even if I **WANTED** to send Lazarus to you with water, I couldn't.

"'There's a deep ditch and there's **NO WAY** he could get to you, and no way you could **EVER** get to him.'

"So the **RICH** man said, 'If you won't send Lazarus to **HELP** me out then at least send him to **WARN** all my friends and family what will happen to them if they live

like **I** did... Pleeeeeeeaase?!'

"But Abraham said, '**NO**. God has told them *again*

and *again*, and they just don't listen.'

"'But they **might** if you send **Lazarus**, or

someone, back from the **DEAD** – Pleeeeeeeaase?!'

"But Abraham said, '**NO**. If they wouldn't **LISTEN**

before, they won't ~~LISTEN~~ now. That's **IT**.'"

Harsh? It feels *pretty* harsh, doesn't it? But Jesus

had a really good reason for telling this story. He wanted

people to see what's really **IMPORTANT** to God.

CHAPTER 17

SIN, SERVICE & SORES

You remember in chapter **15** we talked about **SINNERS**, and way ←back in chapter **5** we talked about **SIN**? Well, Jesus had more to say to his disciples:

"There will always be things that people *BLAME* for their sin. This situation, or that: there'll always be SOME excuse. But, a person who makes another person sin, they'd better watch out. That **KIND** of person would be better off at the bottom of the sea, so be careful that's not you.

"If you see someone who is trying to follow me, and you see them **SIN**, tell them. If they say they're SORRY, then make sure you let them know they're *forgiven*.

" IN FACT ", every time they're SORRY and they really

mean it, KEEP ON forgiving them — no matter

how many times they  mess up."

"But JESUS," the disciples said, "that's almost impossible.

We'd need so MUCH MORE faith to be able to do that."

"If you had faith that was like the TINIEST weeniest seed,

then that'd be enough to tell a whole tree to get up

and plant itself in the sea — and it would do as you'd said.

WHAT
ON EARTH
???

"This kind of thing is just what you're **supposed** to do. You're serving **GOD**. You're working for **HIM**. When you've done what you **should** do, make <u>sure</u> people know you're doing it because you **love** God and want to **SERVE** him."

After this, Jesus and his mates carried on their super **long** walk to **J**erusalem. While they were walking, they heard some random voices shouting. "Jesus! **HELP US**! Jesus!" They looked (around, and there was no one there. Maybe they needed a nap — hearing voices is never good. But then they **REALISED** that if they squinted into the distance they could **just about** make out some people, just standing there. There were ten of them altogether, just standing there, **SHOUTING** at Jesus. **ODD**, right? Well, not really. These people had a *horrid* skin disease, a bit like our guy back in chapter **5**. They were covered in **nasty** sores and scabs. **BLEURGH**. Everyone thought they might *CATCH* it if they got **TOO** close, so they got used to having to **SHOUT** at everyone from miles away. But Jesus just looked at them all and said, "Go and let the PRIEST see you."

So they did. But, **before** they got there they realised they were healed. Their skin was back to normal and they knew they were **WELL**. One of them, a Samaritan, was so amazed and thankful that he couldn't RESIST going back to find Jesus. When he did, he couldn't thank him enough.

He was on his knees in front of Jesus shouting, "THANK YOU, THANK YOU, thank you, THANK YOU!" He hadn't quite realised yet that he didn't have to shout any more, he was right there, with Jesus. But then Jesus said, "There were TEN of you earlier, and you were all HEALED, so how come you're the only one who came back? You're a Samaritan, but you came back to thank me! You can go now. Your faith has made you better." So OFF he went.

The PHARISEES had been asking Jesus when God's kingdom was going to arrive. They were probably trying to catch him out as usual, but Jesus told them that God's kingdom wasn't something they could see, or something that would suddenly arrive, it was something that was already near, with them.

(The kingdom of God? Is God a **KING**? Where's his kingdom then? Well, it's *kind of* complicated. **REALLY**, Jesus is talking about everything being just as God always wanted it to be. He's kind of talking about heaven, and he's kind of talking about earth, but heaven on earth, too.)

That's a *pretty* **HARD** thing to get your head around, so Jesus EXPLAINED it a bit more for his disciples.

"One day, you'll **wish** you could see how it all works out. You'll wish you could see when God sends the Son of Man. But you won't see it. People will tell you to go looking for him, but don't. It'll be like lightning in the sky, all of a sudden.

But BEFORE all that can happen, the Son of Man will be rejected by people and horrible things will happen to him. When the Son of Man is here it'll be like it was for Noah and his ark. People were living their lives, and then all of a sudden everything changed FOR EVER.

It'll be like Lot and his people, too — they were living their lives, but then all of a SUDDEN, when Lot left, that was the END. It'll be just like that when the Son of Man comes."

(What is JESUS talking about? The disciples were expecting him to talk about God's kingdom and here he is talking about NOAH, Lot and the Son of Man. Really, Jesus is telling his disciples that they won't know when God's kingdom will come to earth, but it could be **ANY** day, so they have to be ready.)

"When the **kingdom** comes, there'll be **NO TIME** to go back to the house for anything. The people who try to save (themselves) will be the ones who **don't** manage it. The ones who **lose** their lives will be the ones who are really **SAVED**. Just because people are **CLOSE** to each other it doesn't mean they'll end up in the same place. **Some** will end up in God's kingdom, and others will **NOT**."

"But **HOW** will we know **WHEN** this is going to happen?" the disciples asked Jesus, their knees knocking together.

"When everything is ready, all the signs will make sense."

PHEW. I'm glad it'll all makes sense in the END; there's <u>so much</u> to get your head around, right?

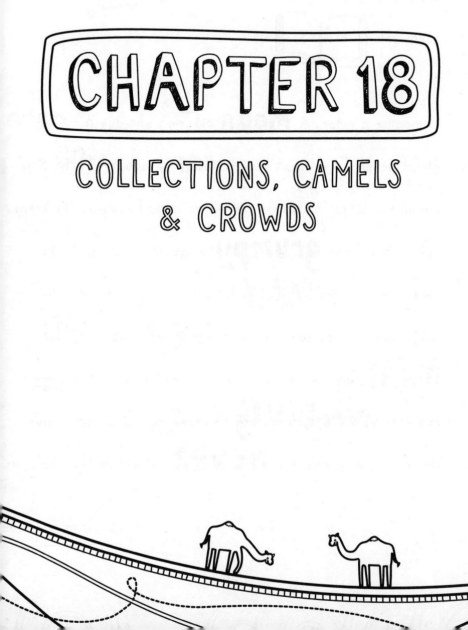

CHAPTER 18

COLLECTIONS, CAMELS & CROWDS

Jesus wanted to remind his disciples to pray, and not to **GIVE UP** praying when things got tough, so he told them this story:

"Imagine a judge. A **mean** old man who doesn't **care** about people, and doesn't even **care** about **GOD**. Now imagine a LITTLE old lady, whose husband has died. She keeps going to see the **grumpy** judge and saying, 'Make sure I'm treated **FAIRLY** in court.' To start with the judge just ignores her. But when she just won't **GO AWAY**, and keeps on coming to see him with the <u>same</u> request, **eventually** he gives in. 'If I don't give her what she wants I'll **NEVER** get rid of her!' he says.

"Think about it," said Jesus. "If EVEN a grumpy old judge helps a woman in need, how much more will God look after people he loves, every day and every night? Of course he will always help them. But when his kingdom comes, will he find anyone who really believes?"

"Let me tell you another story," said Jesus.

"Imagine two men going to the TEMPLE to pray. One of them is a PHARISEE, the other is a tax collector. The Pharisee thinks he's WONDERFUL, and thanks GOD that he's not like that dreadful, slimy tax collector over there. THEN he tells God about all the wonderful things he does for him every week."

The disciples pictured the PHARISEE in their minds.

They knew plenty of people just like him.

"The tax collector thinks he'll NEVER be good enough

for God. He tells God how SORRY he is for all that he's

done wrong and begs God to forgive him. Who do you

think pleased God? The tax collector, of course. If you make

out that you're more IMPORTANT than everyone

else, you'll soon learn that you're not. But if you're humble

and HONEST, that's what God is looking for."

While the disciples were listening to Jesus, a crowd of people

had gathered around them. People had brought their

kids along, because they wanted Jesus to pray for them.

They were seriously **NOISY**: crying and yelling, playing and *RUNNING* around all over the place.

SOME of the disciples had been quietly telling these people *ssssssshhhh* to **GO AWAY** and stop bothering Jesus. "Hey!" shouted Jesus. "Don't send them away. Let the children come to me, don't tell them to go away. They're part of God's **kingdom**. IN FACT, there's so much to learn from them. It's hard to get into God's kingdom unless you're **JUST** like a child yourself."

As the children =*RAN* towards Jesus, one of the men in the crowd spoke up, "Jesus, you're so great. I really want to get to heaven. What do I have to do?"

"Why do you say **I'M** great? Only **GOD** is great," Jesus answered the man. "You know God's rules, don't you? Follow **THOSE**."

"I've (always) followed God's rules, ever since I was a boy."

"Well. There is one **other** thing," said Jesus. "You're a very **RICH** man. You need to sell everything you have and give all your money **away**. Then you'll be rich in {heaven}. Then you can come and follow me." Oh. <u>Not</u> so simple. The man's face fell. He didn't even want to {think about giving **ALL** his money away, let alone all his super **AWESOME** stuff. "It's so **HARD** for a rich person to get into God's kingdom. IN FACT , it'd

258

be easier for a CAMEL to squeeze through the eye of a needle," said Jesus.

WHAT?

The crowd were murmuring: "Well that's it then. How can anyone EVER be saved?" Camels are BIG and FAT; I couldn't even get one through a door, let alone the eye of a needle! Jesus turned to face them all and said:

"There are SO many things that God can do that people can't do." Peter said,

But Jesus, we've already left everything just to follow YOU.

Those who leave everything behind to follow me will be given good things by God, both now and when his kingdom is here.

259

(Sell **everything**!? That's a pretty **BIG** ask, isn't it? The thing is, Jesus wasn't asking the man to sell everything he had because he {thought} he **shouldn't** have any money. What he was <u>actually</u> saying was there needs to be nothing more important in your life than loving God.

That's why just **FOLLOWING** God's rules didn't cut it either; following a set of rules doesn't mean that you **love** God — just that you're **good** at following rules.)

Jesus **gathered** the disciples around him. He wanted to talk to them on their **OWN** about something that they **STILL** didn't understand.

"So, we're on the way to Jerusalem. Everything that's been said about the [Son of Man] will happen when we get there. He'll be handed over, beaten up, made FUN of and eventually he'll be **KILLED**. But three days later he'll be back." The disciples STOOD there and stared at Jesus. What on earth was he on about? ? ? ? ? ?

When they were near a town called Jericho, they saw a MAN sitting at the EDGE of the road, staring into space. They thought he hadn't noticed them at first, but then they realised he was blind.

"What's going ON?" he asked, "I can hear all you people."

People nearby said to the man, "It's that JESUS man, from Nazareth!"

"Jesus! Help me! Jesus! Son of DAVID! HELP ME!" SHOUTED the man.

"Sssshh..." said the disciples. "Stop making such a racket." "JESUS! JESUS!" Said the man.

Jesus stopped and turned. "Bring that man to ME."

Some of the CROWD helped the man up and began to lead him over to Jesus.

What do you want? Jesus asked the man.

Lord, I want to see!

Look and see.

And he COULD! Straight away the man could see.

He couldn't believe his EYES! And he went with Jesus

— thanking God, SHOUTING at the top of his voice:

I can seeeeeeeeeeeeeeeeeeeeeeeeeeeee!

Everyone who had seen what

happened thanked God too. They

were AMAZED.

CHAPTER 19

TREES, TAXES & TEARS

When Jesus got into Jericho, loads of people were just standing there, watching him. Everyone kept *PUSHING* and shoving so they could catch a glimpse of Jesus.

There was one guy, called Zacchaeus (say Za-key-us) whom no one liked because he was a **TAX** collector. Obviously. No one liked having to hand over their money to him, especially when he **always** kept some of it for himself.

Scumbag.

Zacchaeus REALLY wanted to see Jesus, but he was erm... rather short. He tried to jump up high to see above the CROWD, but he could only see shoulders, elbows and dandruff. So he decided to do something just a little bit crazy. He ran as far ahead of the crowd as his LITTLE legs would take him and **climbed**

a tree so that he could crawl out over

everyone and get a look at Jesus.

He got himself nice and comfortable and did his best impression

of a tree. Then something **WEIRD** happened. When

Jesus came near the tree he **STOPPED** and looked up.

Hello, Zacchaeus. Come on <u>down</u>, I'm coming to your house.

Zacchaeus almost fell out of the tree! How did Jesus know he

was there? And now Jesus wanted to come to his **HOUSE**?

No way?! He climbed down as *QUICKLY* as he could and

led Jesus **OFF** to his house, while **worrying** whether

his fish biscuits would be good enough quality.

The crowd stared open-mouthed. "**WHY** is Jesus eating with **HIM**? Zacchaeus is so not a great guy!"

After Jesus had been there for a **while**, Zacchaeus stood up and said, "I'm going to give **HALF** of everything I own to people who don't have enough, and I'm going to **PAY** everyone I stole money from **4** times what I took."

"You and your family are saved," said Jesus. "You've **understood** what this *faith* is really about. The Son of Man came to find people just like you who have lost their way."

When Jesus **LEFT** Zacchaeus' house, crowds of people were still there waiting. Jesus was getting *CLOSER* and *CLOSER* to **J**erusalem and everyone wanted to see what would happen. They'd HEARD Jesus talk about God's

kingdom, and they wanted to know when it would be

arriving. "Let me tell you a story," said Jesus.

"So, imagine a prince who goes off to a country where he

can be made a KING and then comes back. BEFORE he goes

away he gets TEN of his servants together and gives them

a LITTLE bit of money. He tells them to use the LITTLE bit of

money to make more money while he's away. But what

he doesn't know is that ACTUALLY no one wants him

back, because they really don't like him and don't want

him to be their KING. But, the prince came back as king,

and when he he asked each servant how much money

they'd made. Here's how it WORKED out.

Servant **1** says: "I made TEN times as much money."

King says: "Excellent, I can see I can trust with you LITTLE things, so I'm going to give you ten cities to be in charge of."

Servant **2** says: "I made FIVE times as much." King says: "OK, that's good, you can have five cities."

Servant **3** says: "Well, I just (wrapped) your money up and kept it safe in my pocket. I was scared of you, you always take things that aren't yours and I didn't want to upset you." King says: "You IDIOT! Don't you realise what you've just said? You know what kind of man I am, so why didn't you put the money in a bank — at least that way it might have GROWN just a TINY bit by the time I got back."

"So the king told the REST of the servants to take away the money that servant 3 had and to give it to servant 1. 'That's NOT FAIR,' they said, 'he already has ten times what he started with?!'

"'Those who can be TRUSTED with the LITTLE things will be given more. Those who can't will have nothing. Right, now, about those people who didn't want me to be their KING, bring them HERE, I want them ⦃dealt⦄ with.'" When Jesus had Finished telling the story he kept on walking, getting CLOSER to Jerusalem with every step. When they'd nearly arrived at a place called Bethany near a hill called the Mount of Olives, Jesus stopped and turned to his disciples.

271

"I want two of you to go to the NEXT village. When you get there have a look around until you see a young donkey tied up that has NEVER been ridden before. When you find it, untie it and then bring it back here. And if anyone ASKS you what you're doing, just tell them that 'the Lord needs it'."

So that's what EXACTLY what happened next. And sure enough the people who owned the donkey said, "Oi! WHAT are you doing with our donkey?" So the disciples looked at each other and back at the donkey owners, and said with a hopeful smile:, "The LORD needs it." And somehow that made everything OK.

When they got back, they put some of their clothes on

the donkey's back for **JESUS** to sit on and then helped him climb on. Then Jesus on the **DONKEY** and his disciples on their **FEET** walked on towards **J**erusalem.

As they walked, the **CROWDS** at the side of the road **THREW** some of their clothes on the floor so that the donkey could **walk** on them.

DID YOU KNOW:

It sounds *pretty* **WEIRD** that people threw their clothes on the floor so that a donkey could walk on them, right? **ACTUALLY**, this is what Jewish people did when someone important came to town. So what does that tell you about their *thoughts* on Jesus?

273

The people in the crowds were so **happy** because they'd

seen Jesus do so many **AMAZING** things and they

kept **SHOUTING** out good things to God.

> **Blessed** is the **KING** who comes in the name of the **LORD**!

> **Praise** God, Praise God!

> **Blessed** is the king!

> Glory to **GOD**!

Some of the **PHARISEES** in the crowd told Jesus to make

his disciples stop shouting. But Jesus just looked at them

and said: "If they don't shout, then the **ROCKS**

274

will cry out instead." As **J**erusalem came into view, Jesus started to **cry**. As he looked at the city he said:

"Oh, if only you'd **seen** what was going to bring you peace. But now it's too **LATE**, you'll **NEVER** see. Oh, Jerusalem, Jerusalem, your enemies will come and **ATTACK** you, they'll be all around you and they'll completely destroy you. And it's **ALL** because you didn't see that God was coming to save you."

And **SO**, Jesus and his disciples arrived in Jerusalem and Jesus went straight to the **TEMPLE**. The first thing he did was throw **OUT** people who were selling things and tell **everyone** that the Temple was meant for worship.

"It's not a place for ROBBERS to hide!" he shouted.

Every day that followed, Jesus went back to the TEMPLE and taught everyone who came along. But the chief priests and the IMPORTANT Temple teachers got pretty mad. They kept trying to figure out a way to get him KILLED, but it was difficult because so many people were totally hooked on what he was saying.

Things were getting pretty INTENSE. Keep reading to find out more...

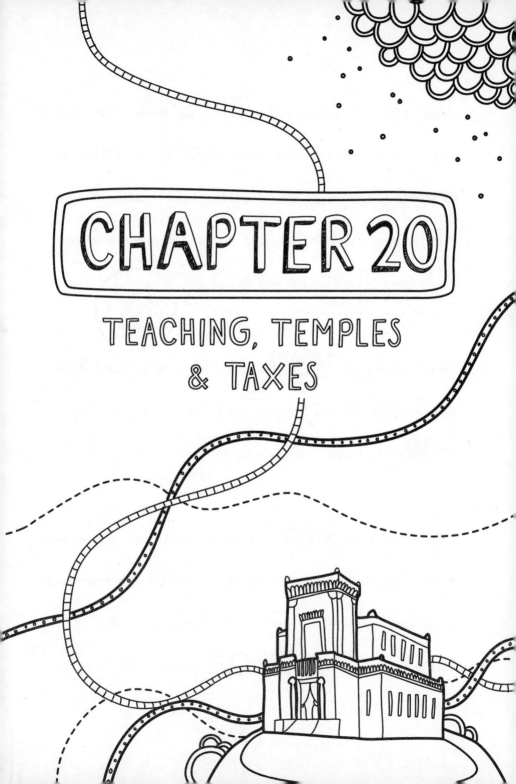

CHAPTER 20

TEACHING, TEMPLES & TAXES

Jesus kept on teaching in the TEMPLE. And the chief priests and Temple teachers got **more** and **more** grumpy. Eventually they decided to have it out with Jesus:

What makes you think you can just stand there and say ALL this? Who said you could?

"Well, let me ask **YOU** a question," said Jesus. "Who said JOHN the Baptist could baptise people? Was it GOD or just some random person?"

They didn't know **WHAT** to say. What kind of answer was that? They knew that if they said it **WAS** God then Jesus would want to know why they didn't *believe* John. But, if they said it was just a RANDOM person, then the crowds would throw rocks at them because they **ALL** believed that

John was sent from God. **TOUGH** choice. "We don't know."

(They *figured* this was the best way to avoid trouble for now.)

"OK. Well in **that** case I'm **NOT** telling you who gave me

the **RIGHT** to do what I'm doing and say what I'm saying."

Clever guy. Jesus turned back to the **CROWDS** in the

Temple and told them another sto ry. The chief priest

and Temple teachers stared at each other and then back at

Jesus. Their faces were super **grumpy**, extra puzzled and

majorly freaked out all at once, but Jesus didn't seem to mind.

"There was **once** a man who owned a vineyard," said Jesus.

(A vineyard is like a GRAPE *farm* where the grapes get turned into wine in the end!)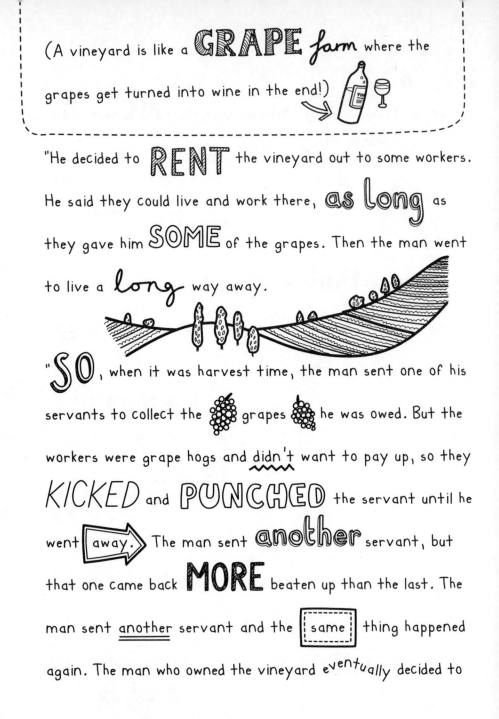

"He decided to RENT the vineyard out to some workers. He said they could live and work there, as long as they gave him SOME of the grapes. Then the man went to live a *long* way away.

"SO, when it was harvest time, the man sent one of his servants to collect the grapes he was owed. But the workers were grape hogs and didn't want to pay up, so they KICKED and PUNCHED the servant until he went away. The man sent another servant, but that one came back MORE beaten up than the last. The man sent another servant and the same thing happened again. The man who owned the vineyard eventually decided to send his OWN son, because surely the workers wouldn't hurt him. But he was **WRONG**. The workers saw the son coming and said to themselves, 'He's going to OWN this vineyard one day, so if we KILL him, then we can keep it.' And that's exactly what they did."

Ouch. Mean story? As usual, Jesus was using a story to help the people understand his message. After he'd finished talking to the crowds, he asked them what THEY thought the owner of the vineyard would do NEXT. What would YOU have done?

"The owner of the vineyard will go back there himself, he'll get RID of those workers and let someone else take over."

(Jesus wanted the people listening to **realise** that the owner of the vineyard was kind of like **GOD**, and the **MEAN** workers were the people who **IGNORE** God and turn away from him.)

No **WAY!** We can never let that happen!

the crowd shouted at Jesus.

But Jesus **looked** at each one of them in the eye and said, "Then why was it written so long ago: 'The **STONE** the builders (don't) choose will become the most important stone of all?' Anyone who falls over this stone will end up in a bad way. And if this stone falls on **TOP** of someone — that'll be the **END** for them."

(STONES? Builders? Falling? What? If you have a Bible – check out: Psalm 118:22. But the IMPORTANT thing here is that Jesus is saying that the stone is him. He's the one people ignored, and he's the one who will become the most important of all.)

The chief PRIESTS and TEMPLE people knew Jesus was saying THEY were the ones who were rejecting him – and they didn't like it. Not only had he just managed to avoid answering their questions, now they were pretty sure he was telling stories that made them look BAD. They wanted to arrest Jesus, but they were proper scared of what the crowds might do. They kept a CLOSE eye on him, looking for every opportunity they could to make him SAY or DO something they could ARREST

him for. They wanted to hand him over to the Roman leaders,

so they hatched a **dirty** sneaky LITTLE plan. They

sent some men to ask Jesus a question that would catch

him out. They reckoned their plan was totally foolproof,

THIS time.

"Jesus, you're our teacher," they said, "we KNOW

that everything you say about what God wants is

true, and you always treat everyone with RESPECT."

But, because Jesus is pretty epic, he already knew they

were trying to trick him, so when they said, "Should we pay

our taxes to Caesar or NOT?" he said, "Show me a coin."

(Caesar was what everyone called the Roman Emperor at the time, so everyone had to pay their taxes to HIM.)

"Whose head is on there?" Jesus asked.

"Caesar's," they said, wondering where Jesus was going with this.

Well, in that case give to Caesar what is Caesar's and give to GOD what is GOD'S.

SERIOUSLY? He'd managed to get out of their trap, again. They couldn't believe it. They would have to hatch a dirtier, sneakier, NOT-SO-LITTLE plan.

285

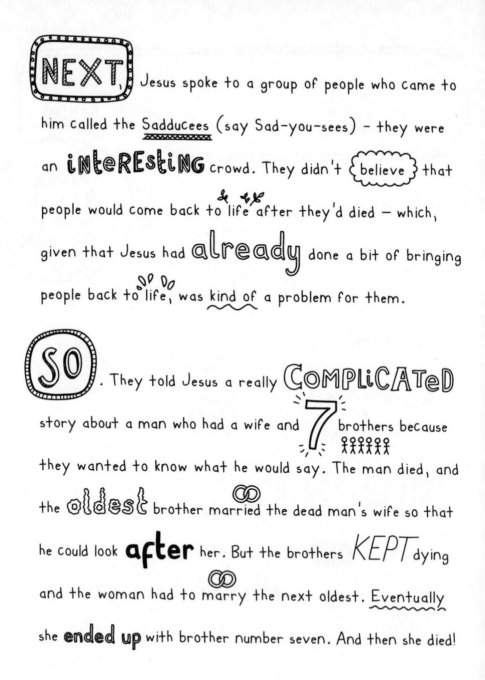

NEXT, Jesus spoke to a group of people who came to him called the Sadducees (say Sad-you-sees) – they were an **iNteREStiNG** crowd. They didn't { believe } that people would come back to life after they'd died – which, given that Jesus had **already** done a bit of bringing people back to life, was kind of a problem for them.

SO. They told Jesus a really **COMPLiCATeD** story about a man who had a wife and **7** brothers because they wanted to know what he would say. The man died, and the **oldest** brother married the dead man's wife so that he could look **after** her. But the brothers **KEPT** dying and the woman had to marry the next oldest. Eventually she **ended up** with brother number seven. And then she died!

(Er, what? That's just the way things worked **back** then. If a **WIDOW** didn't have any children it was the job of her husband's brothers to take care of her.)

They said to Jesus: "So, when this woman comes back to **LIFE** again in heaven, which one of the brothers will be her *husband*?"

"People get married here, in **THIS** world, answered Jesus, "but in **GOD'S kingdom** it doesn't work like that — no one will get married and no one will die. In heaven the people will be like angels and they'll all be God's children. God is the God of the *living* not the dead, just like in the story of Moses. God is the God of Abraham, Isaac and Jacob — remember?"

287

(You can check out the story Jesus is talking about if you have a **Bible**. It's *in Exodus chapter 3.*)

"That is a very GOOD answer to the question," said the Sadducees. After that no one else dared to ask Jesus any questions. So Jesus asked the crowds a question instead.

? ? ? ? ?

"Why do you (think) people say that the Messiah will be the son of **DAVID**? Even <u>David</u> says that the Messiah is his LORD, so how can the Messiah be his son as well?"

(What is a Messiah? Well you might remember way back in chapters 1 and 2 Jesus was described as the Messiah. ESSENTIALLY, the word Messiah means "anointed one" —

someone who is marked out as being *SPECIAL*. Jesus is talking about the **same** David who killed a giant with a pebble, ♪ ouch! and wrote lots of songs. You can find the song he's thinking of in the **Bible**, see **Psalm 110**.) How would <u>you</u> have answered Jesus' question?

Jesus kept on speaking: "You should be **careful**. These people who say they teach the ways God taught to Moses — they **love** to walk around in their fancy clothes; they love it when people **RECOGNISE** them. They always want the **BEST** seats everywhere. But actually, they're **liars** and **cheaters**. They pray **long** and wonderful prayers just to show off. These are the people God will **punish** in the end."

Well. You wouldn't want to be one of **those** people then, would you? Just imagine how <u>they'd</u> be **feeling** right about **NOW...**

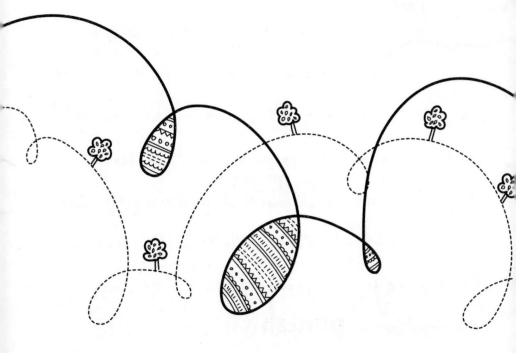

CHAPTER 21

TROUBLE, TEMPLES & TREES

Jesus looked up and glanced around the BUSY Temple.

He noticed a queue of people near the boxes where

people gave their money to GOD. He could see by the way

the rich people just threw their money into the box that

they really wanted everyone to see how much

they were giving and to think they were SUPER

WONDERFUL. Then he spotted a small,

wrinkly, tired Old woman. She took her time walking up to

the box, and when she got there she quietly dropped

just two TINY coins inside.

Jesus turned to the CROWDS and said, "You see that Old

woman? She has given more than any of the others. They only

gave what they didn't need; she gave everything she had."

292

SOME people in the crowd were staring at the different parts of the TEMPLE. It had been made from some of the most *beautiful* stones and jewels.

Oooh isn't it lovely.

AMAZING

"Take a GOOD look," Jesus said to them. "Soon all these stones will be in a PILE on the ground. The Temple will be totally SMASHED up."

"What do you MEAN? The Temple is really STRONG. HOW will we know when all of this will happen?"

Jesus paused for a moment and then gave his answer:

People will come, and they'll (say) that they're me,

But they're **NOT**, you know, make <u>sure</u> you see,

They're imposters, they're *liars*, they're faking it all,

So don't follow them lest you stumble and fall.

There'll be wars, there'll be fights, but don't be afraid,

It's all in the plan that I know **GOD** has made,

These things will happen, but that's not the end,

God's got a PLAN that I'm here to defend.

Earthquakes and FAMINE, **evil** disease,

Way scary skies and trembling knees,

But before these things, you'll end up in jail,

Just 'cause of me, they'll ask for your tale.

So take your CHANCE, tell them of me,

Tell them the things you saw and still see,

I'll give you the WORDS, you'll know what to say,

No one will argue or get in the way.

But do remember this, it won't be much FUN, &

Your friends and your family — they'll turn and run.

They'll dob you in, they'll POINT you out,

People will HATE you, please have no doubt.

But don't be afraid, know I'll be there with you,

Your faith will save you, I say that's "true",

It's believing in me that will PULL you through,

So no matter how TOUGH — I'm (here) for you.

295

When the soldiers come, the time will be near,

So RUN for the mountains, let me be clear,

Leave the CITY, the time has come,

Don't hang around, leave, RUN! ——→

It won't be good, there'll be tears and pain,

Many will DIE, some will be slain,

Some will be taken, some will be lost,

Jerusalem paying a TERRIBLE cost.

The sun, moon and stars, the seas and the tide,

They'll all be so STRANGE that people will hide,

They might pass out, sit in corners and cower,

But everything happening is all God's power.

And then all will see the <u>Son of Man</u> is here,

Above them with clouds, his glory so near,

When all of this happens, be **BRAVE** and stand tall,

Your freedom is here, once and for <u>all</u>!

(Of course, Jesus didn't REALLY say it all so it rhymed like this — but it **HELPS** me to remember the AMAZING things he said!)

While **everyone** was taking it in, Jesus sat down and told another story.

"When you see the TREES starting to sprout, you know that the warmer weather is coming.

"So when you SEE all the things I've talked about starting

to **happen** you'll know what is on the way. God's **kingdom**

will be coming, and SOME of you will even see it for

yourselves. This 🌍 earth and that sky ☁ won't last for ever,

but the words I speak will **NEVER DIE**. So, don't

waste your time worrying or the end will be here and

it'll catch you out. When it all **happens**, it will be a

complete surprise. Keep on praying; keep on looking for all

these things — if you do, the ┃ Son of Man ┃ will be pleased."

People just couldn't **STOP** listening to Jesus. They came

⬅back to the **TEMPLE** every day to hear him. Every

night, Jesus left the Temple and camped out on the Mount

of Olives. **Every day** he was in the Temple bright and

early and ready for a **NEW** day.

Well. That was a whole lot of **AMAZING** stuff.
Some *pretty* scary things too. But I trust
Jesus. I really do. What do **YOU** think about
the things he said?

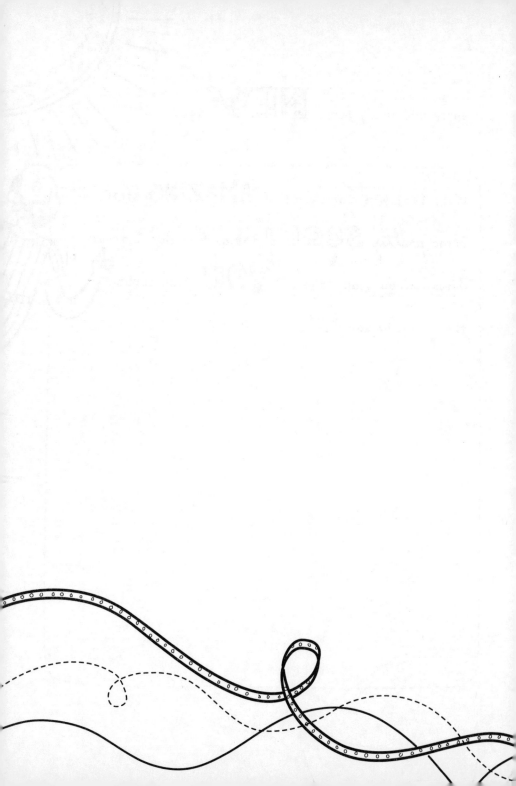

CHAPTER 22

SUPPER, SNEAKING
& SWORDS

The **PASSOVER** was not **many** days away.

(The Passo-*WHAT*? Passover is a Jewish festival. So

every **Jew** in **J**erusalem would've been getting ready

to celebrate it. They'd been **celebrating** Passover for

hundreds and hundreds of years by having a special meal

that reminded them of when their very **ancient** family

was set free from **E**gypt. You can read all about it in the

Bible, if you have one — have a look at **Exodus chapter 12**.)

By now, the chief **PRIESTS** and important **TEMPLE**

people were so, so desperate to get *RID* of Jesus. They were

worried he was going to start turning people against them

and then they'd have even **BIGGER** problems to deal with.

But then, the **DEVIL** got to Judas, one of Jesus' 12 disciples, and persuaded him to :(do): something — something that would change **everything**.

SO Judas went to see the people who wanted to get *RID* of Jesus and **TOGETHER** they made a sneaky plan. Judas ended up with a nice pile of money for his **trouble** — and so he **agreed** to find a time and place when Jesus would be ←away→ from the crowds so that he could captured.

PASSOVER arrived and everyone started to get ready. The first thing they needed to do was **SORT OUT** the lamb for the meal, so Jesus asked **Peter** and **John** to go and make a start.

But they said, "WHERE are we going to eat? WHERE should we go and set everything up?"

"When you go into town, you'll see a man carrying a huge jar of water. Follow him, and when he gets to his HOUSE tell the owner that your teacher wants to know where he can celebrate the PASSOVER with his friends. Then he'll take you upstairs and show you a room where you can get everything ready."

Sure enough, when Peter and John got into town, everything happened JUST LIKE Jesus said it would, which was probably a good thing otherwise Peter and John might've looked pretty STRANGE.

Later on, when it was TIME for the Passover meal, JESUS and his mates sat down to eat. But just before they started, Jesus said something:

I've been really looking forward to having this meal with you guys before everything starts to HAPPEN. I'm going to suffer soon and I won't get to have a meal like THIS until we're all together with GOD.

Jesus picked up a cup of wine from the table, thanked God for it and said: "Pass this around. SHARE it. I won't be having any more wine until God's kingdom is here."

Then Jesus picked up some of the bread from the table and *thanked* God for that, too. He **tore** the bread into pieces and gave it to the disciples and said: "This bread is my BODY. It is BROKEN for you. Eat it as a way of remembering me."

He picked **another** cup of wine, thanked **GOD** for it and said: "This wine is my **blood**. It is poured out for **YOU**. God is using it to make **everything NEW**."

Then Jesus looked **EACH** of the disciples in the eye and said, "The person who is going to **BETRAY** me is here, in this room: it's one of *you*. I will die just as I was **meant** to, but for the person who betrays me it will be horrible."

Everything went *crazy*. The disciples started fighting with each other, trying to find out who would EVER BETRAY Jesus.

I would never do that!

It's NOT me!

Is it you?

What's he talking about, he can't suffer?!!

The disciples carried on fighting and ended up arguing about who was the BEST.

"LOOK," said Jesus, interrupting their argument, "don't be like kings who BOSS people around. Whichever one of you is the *best* should be the *best* at serving everyone else. People think it's the person who is being served that's the most IMPORTANT, but think about it — all the time I've been with you I've been your servant.

"But because you've STOOD by me, even when things have been hard, I want you to know that I will make you like kings, because GOD has made me king over everything. You'll be with me in my kingdom and we'll eat and drink together."

The disciples stopped arguing. This was all starting to sound pretty SERIOUS.

"Simon Peter!" Jesus said loudly. "Listen to me."

"Every one of you will be TESTED when I'm gone. But, Peter, I have asked God to keep your faith STRONG, and when you come back to me, HELP the others."

308

"But Jesus, I'd do anything for you, I'd go to jail for you, I'd even die for you."

"Oh, Peter," said Jesus. "If only you KNEW. Before you hear the cries of the rooster tomorrow morning you'll turn away from me 3 times. You'll say you don't know me."

"Listen, all of you," said Jesus. "When I sent you out and said don't take money or bags or shoes, was there anything that you needed?"

"NO. Not at all," they replied.

"Now it's different. If you've got money, bring it with you.

If you don't have a sword, BUY one. If you've got a

bag, FILL it with all you can and carry it with you.

It was written about me, a *long* time ago, 'People will

{think} he is a criminal.' That's going to be TRUE soon.

That's exactly what they'll think."

The disciples **rummaged** around in their bags and managed

to find 2 swords. "Look, Jesus, we've got two swords!"

"That's **ENOUGH** now," said Jesus, as he began to walk away.

Jesus was heading back towards the Mount of Olives and

the disciples followed him quietly. When they arrived the

ssssshhh

disciples SAT DOWN, and Jesus said to them, "Pray

NOW. Pray that you won't be **tested**."

Then Jesus **kept on** walking and left the disciples behind. Suddenly he **FELL** onto his knees: "God, **PLEASE** don't **make** me do this, *please* don't... But do what **YOU** want to do, not what **I** want."

Jesus was in **SO MUCH** pain that an *angel* appeared and came to help him.

EVENTUALLY, Jesus got up and went back to find his disciples. They were **snoring** their heads off, fast asleep. "_Why_ are you asleep?" he said.

zzzzz zzZzz

"**WHY** were you not praying? Wake up now, and pray that you won't be **tested**." Jesus was still trying to wake the disciples when a **CROWD** of people appeared in the DISTANCE. They were getting closer pretty *QUICKLY* and, as they did, it became **CLEAR** that there was one man out in front. The disciples squinted at him, it looked like **Ju**... but it couldn't be... could it? It was — It was **Judas**.

Judas came *STROLLING* over and gave Jesus an **ENORMOUS** hug and planted a great **BIG** kiss on his cheek. But there was a **strange** look on his face...

Judas, are you **BETRAYING** the Messiah with a kiss?

And then it dawned on the disciples. It had been Judas all along. Jesus was about to be arrested and taken away. They grabbed their swords and RAN towards the crowd. "Shall we attack them, Jesus? Shall we use our swords?"

"NO. Stop. That's enough!" said Jesus as people from the crowd grabbed HOLD of him.

But it was too late for one of the crowd. Someone had swung their sword at him and cut his ear clean OFF. Ew. Jesus simply reached out and touched the man's head and his ear was INSTANTLY healed.

Jesus spoke to the crowd as they tried to lead him away.

"Why are you arresting me like this? **WHY** did you bring all these swords and weapons to *hurt* me? Why are you treating  me like a criminal? I was there every day in the Temple, you could've taken me **away** whenever you wanted. Why **NOW**? Why like **THIS**? This is the time. Now the darkness is in control."

They led Jesus **AWAY**.

Peter **waited** until the crowd had gone off ahead, and then he *followed* them, all the way to the **HOUSE** of the high priest. Once Jesus had disappeared from view, Peter **SNUCK** inside.

After a while, Peter noticed some people were lighting a fire  in the courtyard. So he went over to JOIN them and sat QUIETLY, trying to get WARM.

The people round the fire kept looking at him. Peter buried his FACE in his cloak.

He was with JESUS! one of the women announced.

I was not. I've never even met him, mumbled Peter into his cloak.

Later on someone else said:

Hey! You're that GUY who was with Jesus, aren't you?! You're one of those DISCIPLE people!

315

No I'm **NOT,** said Peter **STOP** saying that I am.

But then, about an *hour later,* someone else spoke up:

"**LOOK** at him, he's clearly from **G**alilee. And that's where that Jesus guy came from. **OF course** he knows him. Don't you?"

Peter **STOOD UP** and shouted, "I DON'T KNOW HIM! Leave me ←alone!"→ And then, just as Peter finished talking, he heard it. A **ROOSTER** crying out loudly.

Just like Jesus said.

COCK-A-DOODLE DO!

COCK-A-DOODLE DO!

Peter turned and saw Jesus over the other side of the

courtyard. Jesus was looking straight back at him. Peter couldn't **STAND** it, he couldn't stand knowing what he'd just done. He turned and ≡RAN away as fast as he could with tears streaming down his face.

Meanwhile, the guards who were keeping an eye on Jesus started to **BULLY** him. They kicked and punched and called him names. They even put a blindfold on him and then took turns **HITTING** him in the face. "Go on then," they jeered, "tell us **WHO** it was that hit you."

COCK-A-DOODLE DO!

After a *pretty* **awful** night, the morning came and Jesus was ═dragged═ before all the important **TEMPLE** people. "Tell us then! Are **YOU** the Messiah?" they sneered.

"If **I** said I was, **YOU'D** say I wasn't," replied Jesus. "If I asked you a *question*, you'd *ignore* me. But you should know that now the ⟦Son of Man⟧ will take his **PLACE** at the right-hand side of God in heaven."

"So **are you** the ⟦Son of Man⟧ then? Is that who you're claiming to be?"

"That's who **YOU** say I am," said Jesus.

"That's **settled** then. We don't need any more witnesses, <u>do we</u>? He's just said it **HIMSELF**."

(What's going on here? Did you notice anything **ODD**

about what just happened to Jesus? Write your thoughts here)

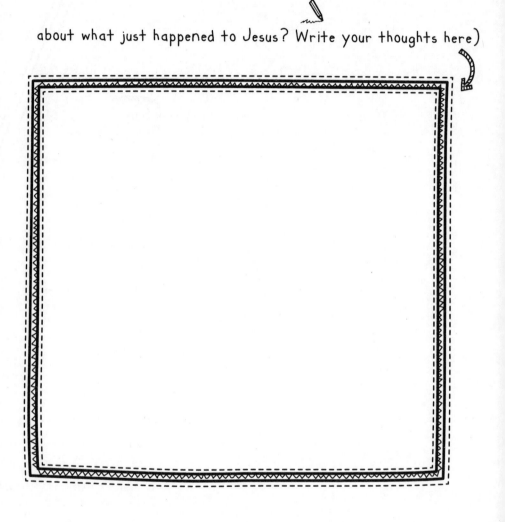

CHAPTER 23

THE END?

SO. They reckoned they'd caught Jesus **GOOD** and **PROPER** this time. He'd said it **himself**, after all, hadn't he? (Had he?)

They *DRAGGED* him off and made him stand up in front of **Pilate** (you remember, the guy from chapter **13**, right?) and started saying **ALL** kinds of things about him. "He **reckons** he's the Messiah, our king!" "And, he **EVEN** told people they didn't have to pay their taxes!"

Pilate looked at the **CROWDS**, and looked at **JESUS**. The crowds looked angry. "Are you the **KING** of the **Jews**?"

322

"That's what **YOU** say," said Jesus.

"I don't think this man has done anything **WRONG**," Pilate told the crowds.

"But he has, he has!" they **SHOUTED** back. "He's been teaching things!" "He's been causing **trouble** everywhere he goes!" "He started in **G**alilee and now he's ⌐here¬ – disturbing **everything**!"

"Are you saying this is a man from **G**alilee?" asked Pilate. "**Right**. Well it's not (my) job to judge 🔨 him then, is it? If he's from Galilee, that's where **Herod** is in charge."

Herod, who just so happened to be visiting Jerusalem, got quite excited when he heard that Jesus was being brought to him. He wanted to see if Jesus would do a miracle for him — just so that he could WATCH. When Jesus arrived, Herod asked him question after question, but Jesus didn't say anything. Because he wasn't speaking, the chief PRIESTS and TEMPLE people started SHOUTING again, saying that Jesus had said and done all kinds of really awful things. They were getting angrier and angrier.

So, after a while, Herod and his guards started saying MEAN things to Jesus and PUSHING him around. They made him wear a fancy cloak and then sent him back ➡ to Pilate. *Herod* and **Pilate** had always hated each other, but now they had something in common

—JESUS.

Pilate pulled **everyone** together, the chief PRIESTS, TEMPLE guys and SOME of the crowds.

"You told me this Jesus was causing trouble everywhere. Well, I've ???? questioned him, and so has *Herod*, and I don't think he deserves to DIE — he's done nothing wrong. I'll have him whipped and that'll be the end of it."

But the crowd SHOUTED, "KILL HIM! KILL HIM! Let someone else go free instead."

"That Barabbas guy, that **murderer** – if you want to let someone get AWAY with what they've done, he'll do!"

(Barabbas was a murderer and he'd been in jail serving his time. It was a tradition that the governor would set one prisoner *free* around the Passover every year, if he wanted.)

Pilate couldn't quite believe what he was hearing. So he told the crowd (again) that Jesus had done nothing wrong.

"Kill him! Kill him! Put him on a CROSS! Crucify him!"

"But WHY? He hasn't done anything! I've TOLD you, I'll get him whipped and beaten up — surely that's enough?"

said Pilate. He was getting *pretty* desperate now. But the **SHOUTING** didn't stop. IN FACT , it got worse and worse, the crowds were truly scary now, and eventually Pilate gave in. He let Barabbas out of jail and gave Jesus to the CROWD.

"Do what you WANT with him," he said, as he walked away.

(Crucify? (say Croo-si-fy) Crucifixion? (say Croo-si-fic-shun) Essentially, a person who is crucified is fastened on to 2 pieces of wood in the shape of a cross, which is stood up in a hole in the ground, and then they are LEFT there until they DIE. Usually the Romans put BIG STRONG nails through their hands and feet so that the people could not escape.

327

They almost ALWAYS took all the clothes off the person on the † cross, too. Crucifixion was a long, slow and painful death and, to make it even worse, when the Romans crucified people they usually did it in a place where everyone could see. And, sometimes, they even made people carry their OWN crosses all the way to the place where it would HAPPEN.)

The soldiers DRAGGED Jesus away. On their way out of the city, they saw a man, called Simon, coming in from the fields, and they grabbed him and made him carry Jesus' cross along the road. Lots of people were still following Jesus, even NOW. Many of the women were crying, and Jesus turned around to face them:

"Don't cry because of me. You should cry for yourselves and your children. There are terrible things coming, much worse than you can imagine. In those days you'll wish you weren't here. If these things are happening to me now when I'm here with you, imagine what will happen when I'm not."

There were 2 more men being crucified that day, and when they reached the place outside the city called The Skull the soldiers fastened the men on to their crosses and lined them up side by side, with JESUS in the middle.

As Jesus hung there on his cross he said, " Father GOD, please, please forgive these people, they don't know what they're DOING."

The soldiers were standing around, waiting for the **END**, and they were **ARGUING** about who should get to keep Jesus' clothes. They were rolling dice to see who would be the winner.

The leaders who had wanted Jesus **DEAD** were standing around and were still **SHOUTING** things at Jesus.

"Look at him. He said he saved people. He can't even save **HIMSELF**, can he? If he's God's Messiah that shouldn't be too **HARD**!"

The soldiers shouted things at Jesus, **TOO**. They even brought him some wine. "If you're the King of the Jews," they said, "come on down and **save** yourself." There was

330

This is the King of the Jews.

a sign above Jesus' head that said:

Even one of the other men being crucified shouted at Jesus.

"You're **supposed** to be the **Messiah**, aren't you? Do some saving then. Save :yourself!: Save (me!")

(Hey!) shouted the other man. "Aren't you **afraid** of God? You're on a cross because of all the ^awful^ things you did. We DESERVE to be here, it's our OWN fault. But this man, this Jesus, he never did anything wrong. Then he said: "Jesus, remember me when you come into your **kingdom**."

Jesus said, "I tell you the TRUTH, I promise that even today you will be with me in PARADISE."

331

At around twelve o'clock **everything** went dark. The sky was black. The sun had stopped shining. Everything stayed **DARK** until the middle of the afternoon, when 'suddenly' the curtain in the Temple tore in TWO and Jesus shouted out: "Father, into **your** hands I place my spirit."

And then he **DIED**.

When the Roman soldier in CHARGE saw what had just happened he called out to GOD. "This man was INNOCENT!"

The crowds began to **leave**. As they went away they were **so, so sad**. Jesus' closest friends and some of the women who had followed him all the way from Galilee stood in the DISTANCE and watched everything that HAPPENED.

(Only the PRIESTS were allowed behind the curtain in the TEMPLE, where they believed God lived. When Jesus died and the curtain was torn in TWO, it meant that all the barriers between ordinary people and GOD had been taken away. Wow.)

A man called **Joseph** from a place called **A**rimathea

was a member of **Pilate's** council. He was a GOOD guy

and he had <u>never</u> been OK with what had happened to Jesus.

So he went to see Pilate and asked if he could take down Jesus'

body from the CROSS. It was the {least} he could do.

Joseph took Jesus' body and wrapped it in *beautiful* cloth.

He then **carefully** carried it to a brand **NEW**

tomb that had been carved out of the ROCKS and laid

Jesus down {inside.} Some of the women were **still**

following behind, and after they'd seen where Joseph had put

Jesus' BODY they went away to get some spices ready.

(Spices helped to stop things from smelling bad when

335

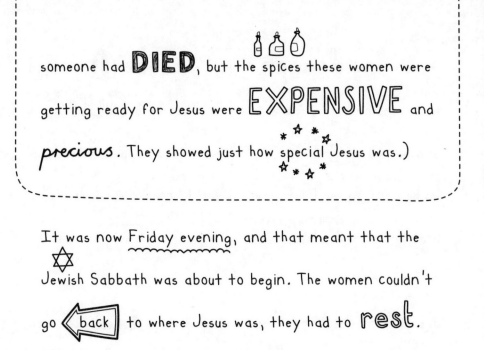

someone had **DIED**, but the spices these women were getting ready for Jesus were EXPENSIVE and *precious*. They showed just how special Jesus was.)

It was now Friday evening, and that meant that the Jewish Sabbath was about to begin. The women couldn't go back to where Jesus was, they had to rest.

CHAPTER 24

NOT THE END!

As SOON as the Sabbath had PASSED the women went straight to Jesus' tomb. They took the spices they'd got ready and left as early as possible on Sunday morning.

When they arrived, the first thing they SAW was the ENORMOUS stone that had been put in front of the place where Jesus' body lay. It wasn't where it had been LEFT. They knew, for sure, that the stone had been in front of the tomb, and now it wasn't. It had been rolled away to one side. Odd.

They went inside, not knowing what to expect, and Jesus' body wasn't there. They checked everywhere, but the body was definitely GONE. Freaky.

338

Two men SUDDENLY appeared from nowhere. They were

SHINY and sort of glowing. (You might remember someone

like this right near the beginning of my [story!]) The

women couldn't (deal) with a missing body and shiny,

glowing, SUDDENLY appearing men, and they just FELL

down onto the floor. They were absolutely TERRIFIED.

Then the men SPOKE.

Why are you looking for someone who is alive in a place

where you find the dead? Jesus isn't here! He's ALIVE,

he's been raised from the DEAD. Just like he said he

would. Think back, remember, when you were with him in

Galilee he said this would happen. He said he'd DIE on

a cross and then he'd come back to life three days later.

The women sat up slowly and began to remember everything that Jesus had said. They couldn't keep it all in and they RAN as FAST as they possibly could, almost tripping over their own feet, to find Jesus' disciples to tell them that it had all come TRUE. When they found them they could hardly speak. They were soooooooooooooooooooooooooooo excited! They told them EXACTLY what had happened. They told them Jesus was alive! But the disciples thought the women were talking a load of rubbish, and didn't believe a word they said.

But Peter wondered. Why would the women be making it up? He left everyone and RAN to the tomb to see for himself. When he looked inside he could only see

340

the cloth Jesus had been wrapped in. Definitely **NO** body.

He made his way ← back to everyone else, and he kept

on **wondering.**

Later on two of the disciples were on their way

to a place called **Emmaus.** (say E-may-uss — not

e-mouse!). They were walking *slowly* along the **ROAD,**

feeling **SORRY** for themselves. They couldn't (stop)

talking and thinking about **everything** that had happened

and they were wearing super sad faces. They didn't know <u>what</u>

to *believe* any more. The man they'd **TRUSTED,** the

man they'd **FOLLOWED,** the man they'd listened to —

he was gone.

Jesus came CLOSE to the disciples, and walked along NEXT to them. For a while they didn't even notice him, but when they did, they didn't recognise him at all. So he started to (talk) to them.

"WHAT are you two talking about?"

They looked at JESUS with their sad faces and then looked at each other with a slightly confused look.

"Are you the ONLY person in the whole of Jerusalem who doesn't know what has just happened?" one of them said.

"MAYBE. What do you MEAN?" said Jesus.

"Everything that happened to :Jesus.: The carpenter's son

from **N**azareth. He did **AMAZING** things and showed

people that he was a messenger from **GOD**. Everyone loved

him. Then the chief **PRIESTS** got him arrested for no

reason — and then they had him ✝ crucified. We { thought } he

was going to be the **ONE** who would set us *free*. We

thought he was the Messiah. But that all ended **3** days ago.

Some of the women who've been following us around reckon they

went to Jesus' (tomb) and his body was **GONE**. They

said some **SHINY** glowing guys told them that Jesus was

ALIVE. Our friend Peter has been to the (tomb) to

check, and he says it was empty, too, but there was

no Jesus anywhere to be found." Jesus

SMILED and said to the disciples:

"Can't you SEE? Why don't you get it? Think about everything you've been told. Surely you knew that the Messiah had to suffer first, before everything was made right?"

Jesus explained everything that GOD'S messengers had said about him, YEARS and YEARS and YEARS before. And they listened to him as they walked. When they were getting close to Emmaus, they slowed down near the HOUSE they were staying in. Jesus seemed to have somewhere else to go, and was about to leave, when the disciples said: "Don't go, STAY here with us. It's late, it'll be dark soon." So Jesus went inside with them and stayed for a while. They all sat down to have a meal together. Jesus picked up the bread from

the table, thanked GOD for it and then passed it around.

The disciples FROZE and stared, and kept on staring! Their eyes grew wider by the second. They SUDDENLY knew exactly who this man was. But before they could (say) anything or (do) anything, Jesus had vanished.

"Of course it was him! Why didn't we realise sooner? The WAY he was speaking, when we were walking... the WAY he told us what had been written about him... it's really him!" Even though it was the middle of the night they knew they had to tell the others. They left straight away and went back to Jerusalem. It was all TRUE! The others needed to know!

When they ARRIVED they found the disciples and a few others all together in a ROOM. They were hiding away and **still** talking about everything that had happened.

By this point, Peter had also seen Jesus, so now everyone was CONVINCED he was alive. The disciples who'd walked from Emmaus shared their story, with smiles that wouldn't leave their faces, even the bit where they hadn't realised who Jesus was until he shared the bread. D'oh. Everyone was talking and *trying* to figure out what was going on when Jesus APPEARED in the middle of the room and said, Hi!

"Aaaaaaaaaah!" said the disciples all together.

Argh!   What!   Oh MY!

They couldn't **believe** their eyes. "HOW did you get

in <u>here</u>?" Their knees were knocking together and they were

seriously SCARED. They <u>thought</u> this Jesus person

must be a ghost.

"Don't be frightened. Why don't you **believe** it?

LOOK at me, come close and see. Touch me, poke me, I'm

REAL. Ghosts don't have skin and bones like I do!"

Jesus held out his hands and his feet and moved around the

room. The disciples just STARED. They were absolutely

blown away.

"I'm hungry," Jesus said. "Have you got any food?"

347

"F-F-F-F-FISH," they managed to say, and passed Jesus a piece to eat. He munched his way through his HUNK of fish while they all just stared at him. Then Jesus said:

"When I was with you BEFORE, I told you everything that had already been said about me, everything that had to HAPPEN. Don't you remember, the writings left behind by God's messengers so long AGO? They said the Messiah would have to DIE and three days later he would be ALIVE again. They said that people everywhere need to go through ME to get to GOD so they can be forgiven. And that starts NOW. You need to tell everyone everything that has happened. You NEED to tell them it's ALL

TRUE. Start <u>here</u>, and <u>now</u>, in Jerusalem, but don't go any *FURTHER* until God sends you the HELP he's promised from heaven."

The disciples followed Jesus out to Bethany, where he prayed and asked GOD for GOOD things for them. As he was praying, God took  him away to heaven. The disciples couldn't STOP telling God how wonderful he was, they couldn't stop SHOUTING out to Jesus with JOY. They made their way back to Jerusalem with enormous, unstoppable grins on their faces and they hung out in the Temple, praising God non-stop.

This wasn't the END at all; it was just the beginning...

DID YOU KNOW that Christians *believe*

Luke's story is far **more** than just that... They believe it's all **100%** true. You can read his [story] for yourself in a **Bible**, you'll find it listed as 'The Gospel of Luke'.

If you'd like to find out **more** about what Christians believe then visit (www.scriptureunion.org.uk) or ask at your local **CHURCH**.

Keep on the lookout for the **NEXT** instalment of 'Diary of a Disciple' - it won't be *long*!

www.diaryofadisciple.org